Residential Land Development Practices

A Textbook on Developing Land into Finished Lots

SECOND EDITION

David E. Johnson, P.E., P.P.

American Society of Civil Engineers
1801 Alexander Bell Drive / Reston, Virginia 20191-4400

Abstract: This manual is the first of its type to instruct the reader on residential land development practices. This step-by-step description of the land development process is based on the professional and practical experiences of the author. Readers will be able to incorporate the forms, contracts, scheduling methods, management techniques, and business strategies into their own business. This second edition of the manual includes information on the basics of residential marketing, land planning concepts, and land development design standards. This book provides valuable insight on the land development industry and presents a business toolbox on how to successfully develop raw land into finished residential lots.

Library of Congress Cataloging-in-Publication Data

Johnson, David E., 1950–
    Residential land development practices : a textbook on developing land into finished lots / David E. Johnson.—2nd ed.
        p.   cm.
    Includes bibliographical references and index.
    ISBN 0-7844-0561-1
    1. Residential real estate. 2. Land subdivision. 3. Real estate development. I. Title
HD1390.5 .J64 2001
333.77—dc21   2001053574

About the Author

David E. Johnson was born in Wichita, Kansas. He holds a Bachelor of Science Degree in Civil Engineering from the West Virginia Institute of Technology. After graduation, he joined Greiner Engineering Sciences in Baltimore, Maryland. After gaining invaluable engineering design experience, he went to work for the Howard County, Maryland Department of Public Works. He was responsible for the review and approval of housing and commercial developments in Howard County and in Columbia, Maryland.

In 1977, Mr. Johnson joined the Technical Services Department of the National Association of Home Builders (NAHB) in Washington, D.C. He was responsible for the land development technical and regulatory issues affecting the building industry. His role at NAHB also included dealing with building codes, energy conservation, architecture, and land use regulations. After leaving NAHB, Mr. Johnson joined the General Development Corporation in Miami, Florida, as their Director of Project Development in the Housing Division. His staff was responsible for the land planning, engineering, architecture, landscape architecture, and regulatory approvals for each housing project. General Development required sufficient lot inventory to satisfy an average of 1,500 housing deliveries per year. He was also responsible for the corporate housing land development activities.

In 1987, he joined the staff of Union Valley Corporation to manage corporate real estate projects. As General Manager and Vice President of Union Valley Corporation, he managed the day-to-day operational and future planning activities for the company.

In 1991, he started his own planning and engineering firm specializing in highest and best use land planning studies and engineering for in-fill and difficult sites. Mr. Johnson is a registered engineer in Maryland, Florida, New Jersey, and Pennsylvania. Mr. Johnson has been a presenter of land development topics at many workshops held throughout the United States for the American Society of Civil Engineers and NAHB.

Acknowledgments

As a home building professional, my goals have always included meeting the needs of the homebuying public and, as a result, achieving social good. My accomplishments are a direct result of having strong family support. I attribute my professional success and dedicate this book to my wife, Karen, and my children, Sara and Mark. I also want to thank my parents, Bernard T. and Vivian L. Johnson for their love, support, and guidance.

Disclaimer

This textbook on residential land development practices is based on the field and management experience of the writer. All of the concepts presented in this textbook have been successfully used by builders and land developers in practical applications. This textbook is not intended to present all available land development management techniques. The figures contained within are a result of working with many professionals on land development projects. The sample contracts contained in this book are to be used as guides in preparing specific project agreements. Binding contract agreements should be prepared and/or reviewed by an attorney.

Contents

Introduction

Land and residential infrastructure costs have risen more than 300% since the end of World War II, while labor, material, financing, and overhead costs have either remained steady or increased slightly as a total percentage of the house-selling price. Because of increasing government regulations and decreasing inventory of available land, this trend will continue. This publication is a comprehensive textbook on how to develop raw land into marketable residential lots and homes.

The land development profession is learned through experience, not taught. Developers and builders use each experience to their benefit during the development of subsequent residential subdivisions. Each housing project developed will add to the experience necessary to become a land developer. Each project will further define the process of regulating, debating, designing, and building residential neighborhoods. Land development experts do not exist. It is the level of experience attained by a developer that can influence the success of a project.

Developing and selling housing lots is highly regulated at all levels of government. The housing industry, including land development, is the only business in which the general public is actively involved in shaping how we live as a society. This textbook uses the tools of the trade to illustrate how to find raw land and develop the land into finished lots. All professionals associated with building our residential neighborhoods can use this book to learn, progress, and better understand the complexities of the residential land development business.

TARGET MARKET

This textbook will benefit a wide spectrum of real estate professionals, including the following:

- The developer, who constructs finished lots from raw land
- The builder, who constructs the houses on a subdivided and/or finished lot

- The engineer, who designs the subdivisions, signs and seals the design plans, and inspects the construction
- The architect/planner, who prepares the house plans and subdivision layout
- Local, regional, state, and/or federal government staff, who review and approve the engineered improvement plans
- The real estate agent, who ultimately have to sell the home on an improved lot
- The home buying public, who buy lots and homes
- The public in general, who may want to influence subdivision designs and approvals
- The planning board, board of adjustment, or council members, who cast their votes on the merits of a subdivision plan and influence how a neighborhood is designed and constructed.

Not everyone is a constituent of the home-buying public. The unidentified new homeowner will rarely publicly advocate for a new housing project. The unhindered entrepreneurial vision of the builder and developer in the pursuit of producing a quality living environment must be preserved. We must learn how to balance all of the vested interest groups involved in the land development process to meet this challenge.

INTENT

It is the intent of this textbook to focus on the land development process that can be utilized by all vested interest groups to ensure that quality living environments are constructed to the benefit of the homeowner.

There are many manuals and textbooks assisting the builder in designing and building a house. There are also many manuals and textbooks prepared by design professionals that teach techniques and ways to design housing projects. This textbook is the only effort to teach a developer how to purchase land and develop the property into buildable lots.

Successful developers will be able to design, construct, and convey subdivided land and make a profit by using the procedures outlined in this textbook. This book outlines a successful management process of developing land on time and within budget. The management reports and methods presented are practical day-to-day tools that have been successfully used in the land development industry.

The cost estimating, conceptual design planning, and approval strategies highlighted in this textbook have been tried and proven by industry professionals. The land development bid process, project management, and operational procedures outlined in this textbook are practical and proven methods of managing a development business. Preparing cost-effective designs, obtaining bids of equal comparison, implementing a project plan in the field, minimizing budget variations, and understanding the best interest of the home buyer can be learned through the information outlined in this textbook.

CHAPTER 1

Land Development Basics

MARKETABLE LOTS

The primary role of the land developer is to continuously maintain an inventory of buildable lots for housing construction. Not unlike any other industry, buying land and developing a product for the marketplace requires good business judgment and a keen sense of producing the product below the price point of comparable products.

Marketable lots are a result of

1. Determining how the property will be used
2. Completing a market study to determine the needs of the builder or the buying public
3. Checking on comparable land values to ensure that the price is consistent with other subdivisions
4. Evaluating the physical conditions of the land and its potential for subdividing
5. Researching local, state, regional, and federal regulations affecting the development potential of the site
6. Understanding the legal issues associated with the land
7. Knowing the cost of development
8. Deciding on the purchase of the land
9. Managing the land development process successfully

PROPERTY USES

A successful land development project is judged by knowing when lots will be released for sale, knowing how quickly the lots can be absorbed by the marketplace, and delivering the project on time. First, however, determine how the property will be used:

1.   Include unimproved raw land in inventory without designs or approvals.
2.   Sell unimproved raw land with approved designs and permits.
3.   Sell approved lots and improved right-of-way infrastructure.
4.   Sell or use approved lots, improved right-of-way, and improved buildable lots.

The uses of land as outlined should be evaluated in preparing business strategies and obtaining capital funding commitments. Pursuing each option would allow a production-oriented business plan because the timing of the sale or use of lots under each scenario would be staggered. It is important to maintain an even production of lots. At the start of each project, a market study of location, housing product, competition, and land values should be completed based on tangible and valid research.

MARKET STUDY

Finding land to meet your business objectives becomes easier once the specific use of the land has been determined. Concentrate on the attributes of the overall community. Evaluate each specific neighborhood for development potential, and evaluate each site within the neighborhood on its highest and best use.

COMMUNITY OVERVIEW

A community overview is prepared by compiling and evaluating available information on employment, income, needs, and other demographic characteristics.

Demographic Analysis

Study the number of households, age distributions, population changes, and population trends.

Housing Factors

Study the housing inventory for owner/occupied units, rental units and the vacancy ratios, trends in residential building activity, the potential demand for the number of units expected to be built, and the annual construction rate of housing units in the community.

Economic Analysis

Study the employment trends, family income distribution, future income distribution, and unemployment rates.

Market survey firms, local chambers of commerce, regional planning boards, the Home Builders Association, and other associated real estate agent groups compile specific economic data on communities, such as employment, population, demographics, and potential income by population segments. Economic surveys are complemented by physically surveying the marketplace, talking with real estate agents familiar with school boundaries, and speaking with local residents to understand the housing market. Read local newspapers for several months while studying the community. Concentrate on the classified, business, and community sections of the newspaper. Drive through the community and identify competition by locating on a map the type of product, prices, and when the models are open.

Community Analysis

Study where people are moving from, the sizes of the families, and why they are moving to the community, and project future employment in the area. This information must be balanced with research on where people relax, their income levels, the number and distribution of families according to their household income, and other social factors. As a result of this research, focus on answering the following questions:

1. Can this community sustain the present building activity?
2. Can increased building activity be absorbed by the community?
3. What is the economic future and income expectancy for the area?
4. What are the future demographic characteristics of the area?

The result of this work will define competitive residential projects by housing type, price, size, features, and absorption rate for each model type.

NEIGHBORHOOD OVERVIEW

After a complete analysis of the community, microanalyze each selected neighborhood within the community. Evaluate the competition in the selected neighborhoods, and ascertain if business objectives can be achieved in that specific marketplace. The true real estate axiom is *location, location, location*. However, evaluate the site location with the critical eye of an adversarial neighborhood group from whom a negative reaction to a new housing project can be expected. To further evaluate neighborhood potential, study local, county, and state new-home magazines. The product, land plan, and zoning requirements should be consistent with surrounding property. Evaluate the community's neighborhood location, school boundaries, and geographic features.

SUMMARY OF RESIDENTIAL MARKET ANALYSIS

- Determine housing needs and land development objectives.
- Document existing economic conditions within the area.
- Forecast the economic conditions of the area.
- Undertake a market study to analyze the housing market.
- Complete a competitive housing study of all current residential projects.
- Complete an affordability analysis comparing income with housing price.

- Summarize site data under consideration.
- Recommend housing sales prices and raw land purchase goals.

MARKET COMPARISON

The housing research strategy graph (Figure 1-1) is a format to show the product comparisons of the competition in the market place. Each series indicated would represent a different project. The proposed product line is strategically located to reflect the business goals of the project. The resulting price points selected will provide the framework required in developing a housing product that will sell in the marketplace. The product line selected is further compared against the competition by using Figure 1-2, a competitive housing market profile. (Figure 1-2 and all subsequent figures are in the appendix of this book.) These factors will provide the microanalysis necessary in preparing a housing design program for the project.

Once several sites have been selected for comparison, organize the research information in a resource file for ease of reference. Figure 1-3 is a list of site evaluation factors and the source from which this information can be obtained. Figure 1-4 is a land evaluation scorebook that factors the attributes of the community and of each individual site. Using the scorebook approach will allow the evaluator to objectively outline the advantages and disadvantages of each site.

SITE ANALYSIS

Evaluating the site constraints of raw land is essential to minimize the financial risk involved in developing the land for housing. To minimize that risk, determine the lot yield and the cost required to properly develop the housing project before

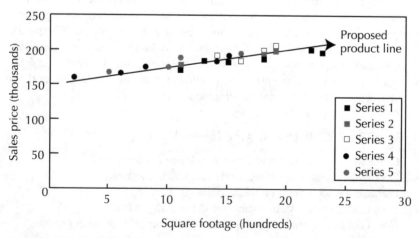

Figure 1-1. Housing Research Strategy

Photo 1-1. Site Analysis. A comprehensive site investigation and analysis of a site will identify the benefits and constraints of a site. This investigation will guide the land planning approach required to obtain the highest and best use for the site.

the purchase is executed. To do this, first undertake a complete comprehensive site analysis study.

Combining this information with other elements outlined in this chapter, the risk factors associated with each parcel under consideration can be reduced.

No two parcels or sites have the same site constraints or development solutions. It is imperative to understand those constraints and solutions so that houses can be delivered on time, absorbed rapidly by the marketplace, and constructed within budget. The more information known about a site and its physical characteristics, the better chance the cost implications will be known, and the success or failure of the project can ultimately be determined.

The results of the in-depth site analysis are the basis for determining the lot yield, preparing the conceptual land plan, understanding the costs associated with the land plan, and selecting the housing product. During the investigative process, strive to identify the unknowns and determine why this property has not been purchased by competitors. As the unknowns are discovered, satisfied, and eliminated, the question "Why does this parcel remain available for sale?" can be answered. The risk of developing that land is further minimized. The next step is to allocate financial resources for further site analysis and site investigative work. Next, rather than focus on the reasons to purchase the property, establish all of the reasons why not to purchase the property. This negative approach will be beneficial during the regulatory process and will help prepare a better product for the marketplace.

SITE ANALYSIS AND THE PURCHASE AGREEMENT

Home building success is based on many factors. Some of the most important factors are the value and cost relationship of raw land and the cost of developing that land for housing products. Ultimately, the site analysis information will be used to prepare the legal documents for the purchase of the land. The purchase agreement should use the identified site constraints as cause to void the contract without financial loss. For instance, if purchasing residential land that uses septic systems, soil test results must be favorable for septic systems. If not, this would be sufficient cause to terminate the contract. The contract should also be contingent on the ability to receive septic permits for construction before closing on the land. Many successful land developers and builders search for small parcels, which are easier to develop. This approach is becoming much more prevalent because of the difficulty in finding land without constraints.

Once a contract has been prepared for the purchase of property and a due-diligence clause has been included, start the comprehensive site analysis work without delay. Obtain the information outlined in Figure 1-3 before visiting the specific sites under consideration. Determining the physical and governmental parameters by which each parcel is governed will give a clear indication of whether the development of that parcel will be successful in the marketplace. Figure 1-5 is a detailed site analysis checklist. If used for the evaluation of land, a clear physical investigation of the site can be documented, illustrated on a plan for further clarification, and used as the basis for purchase decisions. This documentation can be useful when seeking financial commitments from lending institutions and in discussions with regulatory agencies or political groups.

SITE INSPECTION

Once the information has been reviewed, walk the property. Make an assessment of whether the information obtained on the property's topography is accurate. Relate the elevation of the site to the elevation of the existing roads bordering the parcels. For example, if the property falls away from the road or is uphill from the road, the design approach will be different and will have a bearing on the land development cost for the project. The due-diligence clause of a purchase agreement should always contain the need for a soil boring or soil test-pit program. The soil characteristics will affect the site design and will have a direct bearing on the cost of developing the land. The financial success of a project is directly attributed to the existing physical features of the property, such as:

- If there is rock, basements are much more difficult to construct, and underground utilities are more costly to install.
- If there is clay material and if septic systems are used, the clay material may have to be removed and replaced with a different material at significant cost.
- If the site has expansive soils, structural foundation designs for residential housing would be required; the cost of housing and associated liabilities would be much greater.

By walking the property, an assessment must be made to confirm that the general sources of information obtained for the site are generally reliable. If a boundary and topography survey exists before the site inspection, the potential cut-and-fill problems on the site can be documented before design consultants are hired for the project. The soil survey information is necessary in determining the seasonal high water table elevation on the property. This seasonal high water table elevation information is important for:

- Basement construction
- Installation of septic systems
- Dewatering for water and sewer systems
- Locations of unmapped wetland areas

Locating flood plains, fresh water wetlands, and natural drainage swales on the property will guide the drainage design for the project. The amount of buildable area in the project is affected by these environmental constraints. Thus, the profitability of the project can be severely eroded if these site constraints are not addressed during purchase negotiations.

Depending on the location of the natural drainage areas, the land plan of the project could be affected, and in some cases, the property can be effectively rendered useless. Most landowners do not understand how governmental regulations affect the marketability of the land. If there is a flood plain on the property as documented by the Federal Emergency Management Agency (FEMA), the buyer of a lot containing a flood plain will be affected because they will be required to obtain flood insurance.

If the property is wooded, the vegetation growth on the property should be identified and located for several reasons. If the trees are significant in size and type, they will be excellent selling tools and positive attributes for the project. If it is important to save trees for marketing purposes, mark on a field survey where the significant specimen trees are located. This information is essential to the land plan of the subdivision and will also affect clearing prices. If clear cutting is a result of the land plan, the project clearing price per acre will be less, but the aesthetic appearance will suffer. If selective clearing is required to save special trees adjacent to rights-of-way, house envelopes, drainage structures, or utility facilities, the cost for clearing will substantially increase. The benefit of saving specimen trees clearly outweighs the cost associated with selective clearing.

While in the field, note on the boundary survey map the locations of public water distribution lines, fire hydrants, sanitary sewer manholes, electric service, telephone service, and cable television facilities. Indicate the location of each telephone pole located on the roadway. These poles need to be field located in case of conflicts with access drives, road widening, or utility installations. The cost of relocating utility poles can be extremely high. Make note of the frontage roadway width and quality of the pavement. Locate the nearest cross drains in the frontage street to determine if offsite improvement will be required.

SPECIAL CONSIDERATIONS

The following special characteristics need to be noted during the site visit:

- Is there heavy truck or commuter traffic on the frontage road?
- Is there noticeable commercial or military air traffic?
- Is there an unusual noise problem generated from nearby manufacturing plants or tire noise generated from interstate highway traffic?
- Are there any unusual odors present? Note if the odors would pose a negative marketing problem.
- Are the odors from manufacturing plants or from agricultural uses?
- Are there any standing pockets of water? This may indicate wetlands or poor soils.

Take plenty of photographs of the site. Mark on a map the angle in which the pictures were taken. Photograph and describe any unsightly views. Also, photodocument any views essential for the successful marketing of the project, such as a golf course, ocean views, etc. Make note of any demolition requirements and junk or debris removal required on the site. Be certain to look for all environmental concerns on the property, such as 55-gallon drums. Make a clear notation of the compass orientation of the property in relationship to the surrounding land and views. Relate this information to the land plan, and be sensitive to the way the houses would be oriented on the site. During the site visit, walk along the exterior boundary of the property by pacing off distances in the absence of a survey, stakes, or flags. Take photographs of the surrounding area on all sides of the project. This photo history will be useful throughout the planning process.

Find the location of available natural gas lines, and determine if the lines can be extended to the site. Check for the presence of high-tension power lines, if the electric company has future plans to install them, and if easements exist for this type of improvement. Deeds, tax maps, and other information need to be obtained to help identify rights-of-way, easements, or restrictions on the site or on the properties close to the site.

If public water lines are available, check for sufficient pressure to ensure proper fire service for the project. If not, resizing lines, looping water lines, or providing water storage facilities may be required and may increase the costs associated with the development of the property. If individual wells are to be used, find out how deep the wells need to be installed and if the groundwater requires treatment. Discussions with well drillers are important in understanding any problems with individual wells. Their knowledge of the site soil characteristics will be helpful in analyzing the site.

In the site analysis report, assign costs to the various site factors that would affect the development of the property. This cost analysis is essential in comparing the sites under consideration. For site access, determine if there are proper vertical and horizontal site distances at the expected access intersection at the site. Also note whether the frontage road has vertical or horizontal curves or existing vegetation obstructing the line of sight at the access intersection. Determine the future plans of utility companies for extending facilities to the site and the time frame for completion. Determine if the utility services will be consistent with the approval and permitting process for the project. Determine if a schedule problem may result, and include this item as a due-diligence condition of the purchase agreement.

Locate where the public sewer connection would be, and conclude if the lay of the land from the street would allow shallow gravity sewers. A low area within the property may require a pump station solution rather than reliance on balancing the cuts and fills to achieve a gravity sewer. This should be noted on the site analysis report.

The site analysis report should be comprehensive in order to make a sound business decision on the purchase of a site for housing development. Site factors not only identify cost elements but also illustrate potential positive or negative marketing elements of the site. The findings of an in-depth site analysis are the foundation for quality design, efficient planning, cost-effective engineering, and governmental acceptance.

REGULATORY ISSUES

The development of land for housing is the most highly regulated of all businesses. The construction of a home within a subdivision is regulated and governed by the model building codes; whereas land and its use are governed by federal, state, regional, and local regulations and self-imposed covenants and restrictions. These regulations are intended to protect the health, safety, and well-being of the citizens. Regulations affect the quality of our living environment and are intended to reduce the effect new housing may have on municipal services.

EXCESSIVE REGULATIONS

Based on many national studies, excessive regulations significantly increase the cost of housing, and the quality of the living environment is compromised by

Photo 1-2. Regulatory Issues. Governmental permits, standards, and regulations have become increasingly complex and restrictive. Each municipality will review subdivision design approaches differently. To be successful, understand the political and regulatory climate during the market research of the site.

political motives. The additional cost of regulations, imposed at all levels of government, is directly related to the inherent system of delays. The additional cost of developing raw land into finished lots is passed through to the homebuyer. It is common practice to presell a subdivision. The business decision of preselling should be questioned, especially with approval delays, material cost increases, and interest rate fluctuations. It is clear that government regulations will continue to proliferate. The various levels of review will continue to increase and expand and will have a direct effect on the value of approved land. Escalating land values will increase housing costs, and the consumer will continue to bear the cost of overregulation. The result of this cost spiral will effectively eliminate some people from the marketplace. The cost for regulatory reviews and approval delays can represent up to 20% of a new home selling price. Raw land values increase at a steady rate, and the values are not adjusted for the costs incurred during the approval process.

Most builders and developers must borrow capital before initiating a housing project, regardless of its size. The soft costs associated with preparation of design plans, filing applications, and posting review escrows can be overwhelming. The longer it takes to obtain approvals, interest payments will continue to mount. Sustaining overhead costs, monitoring labor costs, and managing material costs must be adequately addressed in the project pro forma by projecting how long it takes to obtain all permits and regulatory approvals. Forecasting cashflow requirements that meet the requirements of the financial institution and the project demands is critical for a builder or developer to hold onto the land during the approval process.

In most states, the model building codes are adopted statewide and not amended at the local level. Builders are aware that the interpretations of code provisions and the costs to comply with code interpretation may not be significant. However, in land development, design criteria and regulations and standards are not only imposed at the local level but can be duplicated regionally and/or by state agencies. There are also inconsistencies in land development regulations between neighboring municipalities. The interpretation and inconsistencies cause unfair competition between developers and affect the marketability of finished lots. In most municipalities, a developer must post escrow money up front to pay municipal consultants or independent experts to review the project engineering designs for compliance with municipal regulations. The reviewing agent often interjects his or her own professional judgment and opinions (which goes beyond the intent of the regulations) into the design. It is this technical conflict that delays the approval of the residential construction plans. It is therefore imperative in the selection of consultants to confirm that they understand the local political and regulatory climate. If the improvement plans can be prepared to meet the requirements, written or unwritten, and approved at the first hearing, the cost of doing business is minimized.

Any regulatory review, beyond the initial review, will add time to the approval process and possibly cause a failure in meeting the closing goals of the company. During the governmental approval process, time is money and the potential loss of business.

APPROVAL PROCESS

Figure 1-6 describes a typical residential construction approval process, illustrating the various steps within all levels of government chartered to process subdivision plans. This flow chart will vary from state to state, but the basic technical requirements imposed for subdivision approvals remain accurate. The timeline has been adjusted to show ranges because of regulatory and regional differences. The only way to compress the approval process is to work with the design consultants and have them embrace the importance of the project goals. When negotiating land purchases, ensure the purchase agreement addresses the regulatory process and the time it takes to obtain permits and approvals before construction. Only consultants can compress the regulatory timeline. If the consultants understand the project business goals, achieve an expedited design review, and comply with the review comments without delay, the project has an excellent chance of being released for sale as scheduled.

DESIGN TEAM

The initial meeting with the design consultant team is used to outline the design concepts for the project. The design approach will ultimately guide the marketing program. The successes in the planning board arena are directly related to knowing the cost of the project and knowing the cost of all technical concessions. Answering questions in a pleasant but direct manner in a public forum and communicating knowledge of the project are key elements to achieving an affirmative vote.

Once the houses and streets are built, the community takes on its own personality. Homeowners take for granted the design and construction of residential infrastructure. They generally are more interested in the housing design, specifications, and style. A sophisticated homebuying consumer will know that location is important to the lot selection and to the present and future value of the lot. The project land plan should be designed to provide choice lot locations, permitting lot premium assessments in each phase of development.

It is appropriate at the conceptual design phase to ensure that the location and orientation of the lots will attract a broad segment of the homebuying public. It is advisable to price the best lot locations higher than the other lots. Initially, sell the less-desirable lots, and keep the best locations off the market until the later phases of construction. If lot premiums are set on well-located lots, buyers will initially gravitate toward the standard lots. If possible, always save the best lots for the last selling phase. This philosophy should be reflected in the land plan and engineering design for the project. Financial resources and time are required to debate excessive residential subdivision regulations. Any concession in land development design criteria can effectively lower development costs and provide an edge in the marketplace.

To obtain design concessions, approach the issue with the multitude of manuals prepared by trade associations and professional groups. Have these manuals available during the discussions with the engineering and planning departments. In most cases, this information will not be well received because the design regulations have been approved by ordinance, and government officials are not likely to change the standards without an overwhelming reason to do so. During the approval process, only adversaries will review and publicly comment on the project. Very rarely will anyone stand up in a public hearing and say, "I like this project," "We should approve this project," or "Let's go forward in providing new houses for the new families moving into our community." Thus it is easier and is prudent business judgment to take the path of least resistance. Achieve approvals as fast as possible to limit soft costs and interest carry for the land. It is easier and more profitable to design a conventional single-family subdivision than it is to seek an approval of a new innovative planning concept.

The risk is great for turning new concepts into a project plan that may or may not be embraced by the homebuying public. As an example, zero lot line housing has a market and is an excellent planning concept to increase density. If the marketplace is not ready for this housing concept, the project will suffer. *Be a leader in design planning, but do not be a pioneer for new ideas.* However, from a cost or marketing perspective, these ideas may prove worth the expense and effort to gain community acceptance. It is rare, however, to find a planning board, board of adjustment, or council that will embrace new concepts for a community without significant public input. Use conventional design approaches, limit the number of design waivers, and, if at all possible, refrain from any variances that would cause debate at a public hearing. The ultimate goal in the land development business is to find a well-located parcel that has zoning in place, a below-market raw land price, and a pro forma showing moderate market absorption while maximizing the profit margin. If any of these land development rules are compromised, be prepared for a prolonged regulatory debate, delay, and increased soft costs.

Over the past 5 to 10 years, the most significant change in the construction approval process has been related to environmental regulations, that is, protection of wetlands, rare vegetation, and endangered species. These regulations affect the way land is designed and developed. Maximizing the highest and best use of the property is directly related to the environmental assessment of the site.

For emphasis, the ideal approach to any land development project is to purchase property below market value, design it in a conventional way to eliminate significant regulatory scrutiny, and gain approvals and permits quickly, without confrontation. Achieve moderate profitability by increasing the sales rate after approvals.

Figure 1-7 is a comprehensive regulatory checklist to be used for the comparison of sites. This regulatory checklist is a guide to be used in getting to know the jurisdiction governing the project from the purchase through the closing of the last lot. It is important to create and maintain a contact file of names, titles, positions, phone numbers, fax numbers, and the secretary's name for each regulatory department. The administrative and secretarial staffs are involved in the day-to-day processing of the project plans. Make their jobs easier by making sure the submission applications are 100% complete. Depending on the project size, absorption, and other factors, most housing projects take several years to complete. Therefore, possible business relationships formed with government officials are key to project success. As the purchaser of the property, personally go to each regulatory department and discuss the specifics of the project with the staff. Do not delegate that responsibility. The more known about the land, the better the chance of successfully developing raw land into finished lots.

VALUE ANALYSIS

Real estate success is dependent on *location, location, location*. In land development, the cost of raw land and the cost of approving and improving land for the ultimate user will determine which location is best suited to meet business objectives.

Figure 1-8 can be used to summarize basic characteristics for each site under consideration and can be used as a general guide to determine which site has the greatest potential for housing. The items regarding reasons for buying or not buying the land will require the developer to be objective in this assessment. List pros and cons with an unbiased perspective. Be very objective in completing this section. List as reasons for buying the land all of the site specifics: location, topography suited for minimizing earthwork, easy road access, excellent vegetation, etc. The list of reasons for not buying the land needs to be completed to ensure the negative viewpoint, if any, has been adequately stated. Every piece of property has a skeleton in its closet. It is the job of the site evaluator or person so charged to find the hidden problems. Determine the reasons not to buy the land. The negative reasons should be listed and the pitfalls highlighted to fully know the development potential of the site. If the history of the land is known, decisions can be made on how to overcome the problems, and the costs can be identified for the solutions. Many failed housing projects can be attributed to paying too much for the raw land at the very start.

Land price comparisons in terms of per acre or per lot are an excellent guide in terms of comparing yields for alternative sites. Most property owners consider the value of their property as much higher than the fair market price as calculated by a builder/developer. This stems from the owners' sentimental attachment to the land. The site analysis and market study will be useful tools in discussing property values with landowners. The regulatory process and housing development standards should be explained in detail to the property owners to assure them that the land price is consistent with approved and unimproved subdivisions. Because of increasing government regulations, the lack of financial commitment to the land development industry, and the competitive nature of regional builders, many projects proceed through partnerships with landowners.

Check comparable land values associated with each site under consideration. Do the research. Orient your project toward the right housing market. Anticipate the time schedule for site selection, governmental approvals, clearing of the first tree, and closing on the first house. Furthermore, understand if the project will be released in an overdeveloped market or a market striving for finished lots. This estimation of time is just as critical to business success as it is to buying the land at the right price.

Investing capital during the site feasibility aspect of the development process is necessary to retain professionals who can assist with the technical aspects of the property. It also gives a certain level of comfort to the developer that a nonbiased opinion of the property potential can be presented with the pluses and minuses of each site. Once the facts are outlined and conclusions reached, proceed toward controlling the property for company use.

CONTRACT PROVISIONS

In purchasing property, the goal should be to hold onto the land as long as possible before closing. Retain the option on the land while obtaining all governmental approvals and permits, and relinquish as little cash as possible to hold the land. Make sure the first phase of the project can obtain governmental approvals quickly and the cashflow requirements can be properly managed. Use Figure 1-9 to highlight those items requiring negotiation between the property owner and the buyer.

All of the information obtained during the market study, the regulatory analysis, the site review, and the value analysis will be used in negotiating the ultimate contract for the land. Similar to land development, the raw land purchase contract should provide an escape clause, provisions, and conditions that provide an avenue to void the deal.

Figure 1-10 presents a land purchase contract outline summarizing the specific items to be included in the purchase agreement. The contingency clause needs to be included in the purchase agreement. This allows the contract to be terminated with cause and without financial loss. Raw land purchase contracts should be prepared by an attorney hired by the purchaser. Most raw land purchases are complex, and legal representation is important to execute the contract provisions consistent with all applicable laws.

CHAPTER 2

Financing

In structuring land development projects, investigate the many forms of financing mechanisms. Joint ventures, installment contracts, and more traditional financing opportunities are available to finance housing projects. Financial planning is an ongoing process that should match the company's commitment for growth. This section provides only an overview of alternative financial approaches for funding land development projects.

FINANCIAL OVERVIEW

Knowledge of the site and of the ultimate use of the property is an essential ingredient in preparation for obtaining financing for the project. A well-conceived project plan, including excellent management skills, management of the cash, and financial resources, is also an essential element of a successful project. Presentation of these elements of the project will be required by all lending institutions.

Because the purchase of raw land offers the greatest potential return on investment of any real estate venture, the selection of an advantageous financing package is important to the operations and financial position of the project. Using any of the alternative financing techniques does not alleviate the need to fully understand the project's financial needs. Undeveloped and unapproved land does not produce income or cashflow. Raw land generates only mortgage payments, interest costs, taxes, insurance, and other payments as dictated by the signed contract. Time is essential in converting raw land to finished lots. The cost of carrying the land until approved and improved may very well drain any profits generated from the initial investment.

Financing land development projects will take many forms and the partnering of diverse interest groups. The typical financing techniques are listed and explained for ease of reference. Conventional financial controls on land develop-

Photo 2-1. Infrastructure Costs. The cost of developing land for residential use will continue to escalate. Material and labor costs are affected by the standards regulating subdivision infrastructure design.

ment projects may become more stringent and inflexible. Thus, developers should investigate the alternative financing techniques for future projects.

ALTERNATIVE FINANCING TECHNIQUES

Purchase Money Mortgage

The purchaser obtains a legal title to the property. The seller takes a mortgage as security by receiving a down payment and in the contract indicates the periodic payments for the principal and interest. If the seller proceeds with the contract and the buyer defaults, the seller will take back the property. The buyer needs to ensure that he or she can walk away from the contract if the loan goes into default. Thus, for developing raw land, design a way out of a project and do not put design dollars into the project unless all certainties are proven. A proper business approach would include contractual provisions that provide escape clauses in case all valued market estimates, opinions, and anticipated market conditions fail to materialize.

Options

For a negotiated price, the buyer obtains exclusive rights, for a fixed period of time, to buy land. The seller retains full ownership until the buyer exercises the option. If the buyer realizes adverse market conditions, the buyer can get out of the contract and suffer only the financial loss of the option price. This is an inexpensive way to control property over a period of time, allowing for favorable market conditions, rezoning, approvals, etc.

Installment Contracts

The seller retains ownership of the property but prepares a negotiated down payment with the buyer and lists subsequent payments of principal and interest. This would be typical with landowners who can retain ownership of the land and have no real need to sell the land, such as with a purchase money mortgage.

Leasehold Arrangements and Lease Options

This approach is a buyer's arrangement with the seller with whom an outright purchase is not possible.

The Land Sale Lease Back

This technique provides an opportunity to sell the land purchase contract to an investor, who then leases the land back to the developer for the eventual development of the property.

Limited Partnership

The developer or general partner provides the management overhead and expertise to manage the partnership and its business activities. The investors provide the funding. The risk is spread to those involved in the limited partnership activities.

Syndications

Syndications raise capital resources through numerous investors. The syndicator manages and invests the cash raised. There are many regulatory disclosures and requirements imposed on syndications.

Joint Ventures

A joint venture is an excellent technique for joining forces of the landowner with those of the land developer. The developer and landowner split a piece of the pie, and the joint venture structure can reduce the financial liability of the developer. The profits, losses, and liabilities can be allocated to each specific project. The specifics of each joint venture agreement must be clearly defined in the contract agreement. Even for large companies, the joint venture financing approach is probably the best technique to be used in the future for developing land in almost every state in the country. Use the following checklist in structuring real estate joint venture agreements:

1. Start and term of joint venture

2. Powers of joint venture group
   a. Right to hold title
   b. Acquire, lease, or sell real property
   c. Borrow or lend funds
   d. Pledge assets
   e. Enter into contracts
   f. Hire employees
   g. Retain consultants
   h. Enhance joint venture business
3. Definition of role of joint venture partners
4. Indemnification clause
5. Management control
6. Contribution to the venture group
7. Fiscal year definition
8. Accounting responsibilities
9. Arbitration provisions
10. Distribution of profits and losses
11. Buyout provisions
12. Transfer of interests
13. Termination clauses
14. Execution

Each state will interpret the laws governing joint ventures differently. A joint venture is an association of two or more people carrying out a single activity for profit. It requires a common interest in that purpose, and the parties have the same right to direct and manage the conduct of each other in connection with the activity. Expecting profit and sharing of the management roles is an essential element of the joint venture. If the agreement does not include a definition of the sharing of any profits, the agreement would imply equal sharing among the joint venture partners.

Blanket Mortgage

A blanket mortgage is for more than one parcel of real estate and is generally associated with single family housing projects. The lending institution releases individual parcels or lots from the lien on the property by the lender.

Other Financing Techniques

Short-term financing, interim financing, open-ended commitments, commitments with guarantees, and permanent take-out commitments, including the financing options, are recognized financing instruments. These approaches can be discussed with accounting consultants or lending institution representatives for more detailed information. These approaches are reviewed for short-term and interim financing requests, whether the commitment is an open-ended commitment, commitment with guarantees from the developer, or a permanent take-out commitment that is converted at the completion of a project into a permanent mortgage loan.

Once the financing package or technique is considered for a single-family subdivision project, investigate what the lending institutions are looking for in terms of presentations by the developer. Developers need to understand the mentality of the lender. Simply, lenders are looking to be repaid and not to take back the property. Also, lenders need for developers to understand the bureaucracy and the time it takes to process a loan request. Lenders require capital investment in the project by the requestor.

CHOOSING A LENDER

It is just as important to qualify the lender as it is for the lender to qualify the developer. Learn what the lender is looking for in the loan submission package so the submission will answer many of the lender's questions up front. This shows that the developer has done their homework in preparing a professional approach to the project while the needs of the lender are accommodated. Preselecting the lender is important to limit the amount of time and effort in presenting the loan request. A blind mass distribution of the loan package to lenders will give the impression of shopping around and the impression of desperation for financial support. Therefore, preselecting lenders and concentrating activities, energies, and cash toward the development of the proper approach for a select few lenders will give a higher rate of success in obtaining a loan commitment.

In selecting the lenders most likely to qualify a developer for a project, use the following guide for qualifying the lender:

1. Evaluate all of the available financial sources, that is, a commercial bank, a real estate investment trust, joint venture possibilities, private investors, etc.
2. Ask for the lender's references.
3. Determine the amount of funds available or the amount that has been set aside for real estate lending.
4. Determine the maximum loan size and credit extended to one borrower and determine if the loan request is within those limits.
5. Determine the percent of capital that can be invested in the real estate industry or real state loans. What is the current investment limit?
6. Determine whether the lending institutions have any loan problems or are under review at the state or federal level.
7. Determine the internal policies, practices, and/or regulations for real estate lending.
8. Determine and review the current real estate loan portfolio and the list of clients.
9. Determine the lender's geographic capabilities and if interstate lending loan practices are available.

10. Obtain, if possible, a sample loan approval or submission package.
11. Determine the processing requirements of the loan package.

The best time to determine who is lending funds for land development and building activities is during the market research and site analysis stages. Visit competitive projects and look for job site signs indicating the financial institution partner for the project. Network at the Home Builders Association meetings. Contact real estate agents and brokers and meet with the competitors to understand who is and who is not lending. Assess each lender's strengths and weaknesses. Understand the bureaucratic approach of each lender to a housing project. Assess the attitude of the institution toward builders and developers

During the loan submission process, again evaluate the lender's current record in lending for residential developments. The substantial upfront costs for project planning, including consulting fees, application fees, and escrow fees, require an understanding of the lender's policy on financing these costs. If the lender would cover start-up costs, the amount of capital infusion into the project by the borrower would be limited. Also, determine how overhead costs are included in the financing package. During the initial discussions with the lender, ask about the performance bond capabilities of that lender. Ask how the performance bonds can be included in the loan package. In real estate, the most important policy of the lending institution is how a performing loan becomes a troubled loan and what the ramifications would be to troubled loans. Know this policy before submitting the loan package.

Once you have selected the lenders to which you will apply, be prepared to submit a complete loan package. Remember, lenders look for professionalism when qualifying builder/developers. Lenders appreciate borrowers whose standards include proven business practices. Adhering to the lending institution's paperwork requirements for a relatively small project is just as significant as that required for a large project. To minimize the paperwork, develop efficient ways to keep the lending institution informed of the financial status of the job.

LOAN PACKAGE

Submit a Complete Loan Package

This approach illustrates the requestor's ability to provide correct and complete information the first time. The lender's comfort level is directly associated with the credibility of the presentation at the very beginning. The following outlines the basics of a loan submission package:

Cover letter. The first element of the loan package is the cover letter, which should contain a brief description and location of the proposed project. Give a brief summary of the financial request and highlights of the project. Be positive, to the point, and brief. The cover letter should be approximately one page in length and no longer than two pages. Determine the specific person who will be reviewing the initial loan submission package. The cover letter should be personalized, and the loan package should be submitted directly to that person. Call the reviewer to schedule follow-up meetings once the loan package has been submitted.

Loan summary. A one-page summary of the loan request is important for the lender to immediately recognize the limits of the request and how it conforms to the institution's rules, regulations, and lending policies. Provide a summary of the transaction parameters with an outline about collateral and the type of financing requested. Indicate the timing for the project and any other important information that the bank would need to act on the loan request.

Project elements. This section should also be brief and to the point. The overall tone of the loan package should be positive and enthusiastic about the project. List and identify the housing types to be constructed in the project. Define the target market and the price range of the product. A location map should be included in the package for the lender to assess the importance of the project location. Define the absorption rate and outline the reasons why this project will succeed.

Company history. Include a summary of the company's experience in the housing industry. Highlight the experience with the proposed product type. The personal financial capabilities and credit history of the borrower and of the company need to be outlined in the loan package. Additional information concerning any community activities, key staff members, and their credentials should be included in the request. List all of the investors.

Marketing strategy. Include an executive summary of the market study prepared, as outlined in Chapter 1. The executive summary is a concise statement outlining the highlights and conclusions of the market research. This, of course, would include the geographic market area, the demographics, the building activity, the trends in the marketplace, and the projections supporting the financial request.

Project team member list. List the consultants that have been retained to provide consulting services for designing, planning, and permitting the project. The various disciplines should include the engineer, soils engineer, surveyor, environmentalist, planner, architect, marketing consultant, ad agency, public relations agency, and interior decorator. A brief list of these firms and key individuals would assist the bank in understanding the commitment to the project by retaining well-qualified people to implement the project plans.

Graph of competitive product. Provide a brief and concise graph of the proposed product versus the product of the competition. Also include in the package the summary of the site analysis. Show how the project will use existing infrastructure and be consistent with municipal master plans.

Target market. Include a one-page summary of the target market. This summary should also be brief and concise. The description of the target market would include a listing of the age ranges, the family composition, income levels, employment characteristics, lifestyle information, and financial capabilities of the market.

Product. Summarize in one page the product line proposed for the project. This summary would include the product design, house layout, subdivision layout, density, size of the units, and product specifications. Highlight certain features of the product that would show how the proposed housing product has a greater value than the competition. Emphasize the pricing and absorption levels proposed for the project.

Appraisal. Include the most recent appraisal of the property.

Sales and marketing. Include a list of the top sales agents, their experience levels, credentials, and resumes. Outline the advertising and promotional program for the project. Include brochures and other material supporting the marketing approach.

Pro forma. Figures 2-1 and 2-2 are project pro formas summarizing the cashflow requirements anticipated for the probable scenario and the most conservative scenario. In terms of support documentation, each line item should have backup schedules. Provide detailed cashflow scenarios that represent the most probable case and the most conservative and worst case for the bank to analyze. These pro formas should be prepared using computers and available spreadsheet software specifically designed for builder/developers. They are not only beneficial for the presentation of a loan request, but they will provide a means of keeping track of the project progress during construction. Backup schedules would be required to show how the costs were calculated for each expense line item. This detailed cost analysis approach is beneficial to the investor and/or lender for their objective review of the project's potential.

Corporate reports. Include any reports generated by the company for similar types of projects. This may include weekly reporting of traffic and sales information. Also, construction schedules and accounting reports are necessary for the bank to review. The bank will determine if the reports are sufficient in detail for proper monitoring of the project. Provide a methodology or a means of reporting the construction activities on a continuous basis to the lender. In essence, develop a management report that provides the sales, absorption, and actual cost versus budget analysis for the project. This financial report is the best way to keep the lender informed as the project progresses.

Financial documents. Include any corporate or personal financial statements and any other bank financial references. List the contact person who would be called for follow-up discussions and subsequent meetings.

Miscellaneous. Also include in the loan package a set of improvement plans prepared for the project. The plans would include the final plat, engineering plans, landscaping plans, environmental reports, aerial photos, renderings of the product, floor plans of the product, photos of the site, photos of surrounding areas, and project schedules. The schedules would include land development operations and the project schedule to close the first house.

Each company will have a certain strength that should be presented with enthusiasm in the loan package. It is suggested that the loan package documentation be prepared with professional flare with the use of computer desktop publishing. An excellent visual presentation of the material would also be beneficial during the review process.

A good first impression will help support and add credibility to the facts and figures that are used by the bank in passing judgment on the loan submission package.

CHAPTER 3

Schedules

PROJECT ACTIVITY SCHEDULE

Developing raw land into finished lots is an art. It can be financially rewarding as long as the project stays on schedule and stays within budget. This chapter is dedicated to the various practical scheduling techniques that can be implemented for residential housing developments. The intent is not to present a sophisticated critical path method (CPM) or a sophisticated program evaluation and review technique (PERT) scheduling method but to illustrate proven scheduling techniques that can be used to keep track of the work production. Schedules are valuable when used on a regular basis. Figure 3-1 is a comprehensive activity schedule for tracking a project from the land acquisition phase through the final transfer of land improvements to local government. This activity list represents an example of the time frame for each housing activity. There are many activities that run parallel with each other. These time frames are based on experience in bringing to market more than 10,000 approved housing units over the past 20 years. To expedite any project, select those activities in which the time frame can be modified. As an example, the consultants retained will require a certain time frame to prepare the designs. However, this is an area in which the time frame can be accelerated. Consultants make money by completing projects in a timely manner in order to have staff available for the next project. Ask them to expedite the project. Once the project has been submitted to the regulatory agencies, the ability to accelerate the permit process becomes very difficult, if not impossible. Successful projects must be managed, and the developer should personally manage the schedule of the project. The regulatory process and public hearings can be managed successfully by keeping track of details.

The activity chart in Figure 3-1 shows a timeline that can be used during contract negotiations and used to determine the contractual time limits for the project. The first phase, the conceptual design, will illustrate the project design parameters. Because the plan will dictate project costs, the conceptual design should be approved by company staff members before the expenditure of funds for the preliminary and final design phases. On completion of the improvement design, initiate the regulatory process at all appropriate levels of government that are required to review the improvement plans. When government agencies provide a review letter seeking additional information or requesting revisions, the plans must be resubmitted as quickly as possible. The ability to transform regulatory issues into project objectives is a critical element in responding to regulatory recommendations. Keep the pressure on government to efficiently review, approve, and permit the housing project. If the response is not completed in an expeditious fashion, the project may receive a lower review priority, and subsequent resubmissions, if required, may not receive proper governmental response. Therefore, it is incumbent on the developer to ensure that the consulting team responds effectively, efficiently, and quickly to governmental problems and issues. Consultants need to design the plans in accordance with regulatory standards in order to avoid resubmissions.

TIME IS MONEY

Another part of this activity chart that requires attention is the ultimate acceptance of the public right-of-way or public facility improvements. The acceptance of residential infrastructure has become a difficult, time-consuming, and costly process. Those companies that can manage and document regulatory inspections and punch lists will have a better chance to turn over public improvements. It becomes difficult to schedule land development contractors to take care of a punch list, especially if the contractor is no longer on the job site. To obtain a performance bond release, companies need to respond quickly to the government punch list. Thus, the developer should hold a land development retainer to ensure the punch list items are completed in a timely manner.

The key to finishing a housing project and its land development improvements is to turn the infrastructure over to the government entity as quickly as possible. Inspect construction to ensure quality is maintained. If it is apparent that quality control is present, government officials will not question the quality, and therefore the punch list items can be minimized. In subsequent chapters, the quality of land development construction will be reviewed. Quality infrastructure does not necessarily cost more, but it provides the ability to manage the project costs and cashflow while maintaining the company reputation in the community. A developer's reputation is the ultimate marketing tool.

Developing a single-family subdivision is similar to producing a product at a manufacturing plant. The raw land enters the plant door; goes through design, costing, bidding, permitting, and construction phases before being approved to leave the plant; and is then finished and wrapped with the keys handed to customers. A manufacturing process of delivering houses on a continuous basis is

Photo 3-1. Utilities. Housing projects are served by various public utilities. These entities work at their own pace and prepare their own project schedules. Contact all utility companies early in the planning stages to seek their input on design elements. Also determine their project submission requirements and determine the installation schedule for the project.

Photo 3-2. Scheduling. Proper scheduling of a project requires daily maintenance of the schedule. This management approach will provide a method to
discover problem areas before becoming problems. The goal of land development is to close homes on time and within budget.

predicated on the fact that gaps or lapses in the production schedule do not delay
production. Production gaps do affect a company's financial stability, employment base, and reputation.

MASTER SCHEDULES

Figure 3-2 is an overall project master schedule that provides a scheduling
overview for a number of projects. This approach highlights key elements of the
project completion schedule from the land planning phase through to the certificate of occupancy. The first certificate of occupancy and the first closing inject
cashflow back into the company. Monitor the progress of each project within the
inventory so that closings can be predicted and production gaps minimized. Figure 3-3 is an illustration of an individual project master schedule, which presents
projected due dates for each major activity line item in the development process.
It also shows the actual dates of completion for each line item. A quick review of
the schedule will identify those projects ahead of schedule and those projects in
serious trouble. At the land acquisition stage, this scheduling methodology is
very useful in predicting the first closing in the project. After completing the
project master schedule, work backwards to establish a start date, and use this

information at the land purchase negotiation table. The growth of a land development company is contingent on complete understanding of the regulatory process and its effect on the delivery of finished lots. The project master schedule would highlight submission due dates for regulatory agencies. The submission dates are important because most agencies require a certain amount of time to review plans before official action is taken. If these submission dates are not met by the consulting team, delays in the project planning process will occur. By missing a scheduled submission date, the project could be delayed 2 to 4 weeks. A delay caused by a missed scheduled due date may affect the project schedule even more if seasonal concerns (winter, rainy season, temperatures, etc.) influence operations.

PROJECT SCHEDULES

Figure 3-4 is a land development project schedule highlighting the major activities of a housing project. This format can be adapted to any project consistent with the company's business plans. All of the major land development activities are listed on this chart. Track the various activities on a daily, weekly, or monthly basis. The actual progress can be illustrated on the schedule. Highlight work stoppages or delays and indicate if there are liquidated damages to be charged against any subcontractor. Highlight milestones for each activity on a weekly basis, including the percent completion of each activity. This management tool helps in managing the work progress and in the approving and processing of invoices. Illustrate on the schedule any problem areas that must be resolved by a business, regulatory, or permitting decision. The time it takes to complete a land development activity is illustrated on the schedule. As work progresses in the field, there are certain ways these work activities can be tracked in an illustrative way and then easily transferred into this management report, as described in Chapter 13. Projecting from the site analysis phase, a master schedule can be prepared using industry production ranges outlined in the land development production table.

The projected land development schedule can be prepared with a conceptual land plan. This timetable would be used as a guide and, when added to the house timeline, would provide an estimate for the closing of the first house. Depending on the time of year for construction, factor in slack days for weather, holidays, hunting season, etc. The labor production rates will also fluctuate with the crew's skill level for each land development activity. Alter these ranges to fit site conditions, quality of the workmanship, and quality of the available labor force.

In production housing, a rule of thumb used in project planning is to allow land development construction activities to precede housing activities by approximately 3 months. This would permit underground utility work, road construction, and electric/telephone installations to be completed for each phase of construction. Proceeding with land development before housing construction will eliminate any confusion onsite and any conflicts between housing subcontractors,

Table 3-1. Land Development Production Chart. In preparing an approximate land development schedule at the conceptual land planning phase, the following daily equipment and labor production rates can be used.

Clearing	0.5 to 1.5 acre/day	Clearing depends on the maturity of the site, the species of tree, and the density of growth.
Excavation	1,000 to 2,000 yd³/day	This activity varies by soil type and design. The range is based on using a front-end loader and trucks to move the material. The production could be increased by 100% if pans are used and the design anticipates the use of this type of equipment.
Sewer	300 to 400 ft/day	This production rate is based on installing an 8-inch sewer line at a depth less than 8 ft. Contractors specializing in underground utility installations can provide lower unit prices and increase in the production rate to more than 900 ft/day.
Water	500-1,000 ft/day	This daily production rate is higher than any underground utility because of the constant depth of construction. Also, greater installation distances can be achieved without interruptions. Design and soil type can affect the rate.
Drainage	200-600 ft/day	This production rate is for the smaller pipe sizes up to 30 inches. As pipe sizes increase and the number of junction points increase, the daily production rates will decrease. The type of pipe material will also affect the rate.
Curb	700-1,000 ft/day	This production rate is based on straight-line concrete barrier curb installation. For Belgium block or mountable curb installations, the rate of installation will increase with the level of experience of the curb crews.
Paving	3,000-4,500 yd²/day	This production rate is based on a residential roadway specification. Contractors specializing in residential paving will have experienced labor and equipment available to pave up to 10,000 yd³/day.

material suppliers, and land development contractors. It is always preferable to start housing construction after the site is stabilized. This will allow the housing subcontractors to have easy access to each home under construction. In addition, the advance site preparation allows the potential homebuyer and the buyers in contract to do a site inspection of the homes while under construction without conflict with land development equipment. Access to the homes under construction and site inspections of available lots will encourage referrals. It is beneficial to market homes when land development housing construction is underway. Schedule land development activities to complement the housing production schedule for each housing delivery.

HOUSING INVENTORY SCHEDULE

Figure 3-5 is an overall approach to tracking the housing inventory by project. This housing production schedule can track each housing sequence under construction. List either the lot and block or track each house by a sequence number in each phase of the project. This schedule tracks each unit by the original start date and the actual/forecasted date. It also lists, by month, the completions, closings, and inventory units, which should be limited to models. This report also tracks sales orders and sales backlog with the starts and closings. By following this format on a month-to-month basis, a company can assess the need to start purchasing new raw land or approved housing projects to supplement any shortfalls in housing production.

With the use of personal computers, it is easier to develop schedules and reports to assist in the overall management of a housing project. There are many software packages available for scheduling housing construction and very few programs for land development scheduling. Because the land development tasks vary considerably for each project, many developers will continue to prepare land development scheduling by hand. A manual scheduling practice requires daily hands-on knowledge of the development work. The delegation of this responsibility to an onsite superintendent should relieve the owner from reviewing the schedule on a daily basis. A daily review is necessary because land development contractors can spend tremendous sums of money in a short period of time. Also, delays should be expected during the normal progress of a land development project. Many of the problems that occur onsite are not tracked or described on a management report until after the fact. The land development schedule provides a means to track project status versus value received and to track problems daily. The schedule can consolidate the progress of various subcontractors, rain days, or problem delays on one management form. This schedule also provides a historical accounting of the project and can be used to assist in the proper management of the next land development project. This historical information also provides a comparison of work productivity of the subcontractors. Their ability to get the job done on time and according to the contract agreement is an excellent reference for future work. The schedule should incorporate the contractors' schedule and should be agreed on before the mobilization of equipment. If properly used during land development, developers will maintain control of their job, minimize delays, and reduce extras. This will result in completing the land development work on time and within budget.

CHAPTER 4

Basics of Residential Marketing

In this chapter, engineers, builders, and developers will gain insight into residential marketing and will learn product selection tips that can be used for all residential projects.

The engineer needs to understand the target market that the project design must attract. The subdivision design approach is certainly different for the first-time homebuyer versus the move-down buyer—the retirement market. The engineer needs to understand the marketing hot buttons that can be incorporated into the subdivision design to enhance the curb appeal and increase absorption.

A successful subdivision will not only have the housing design set the style of the development, but significant subdivision differences between competitors will be more important to attract buyers. The amenities and ambiance of the subdivision design should be a memory point for the homebuyers. Creative subdivision design and not innovative design will be best suited for the planning of housing projects.

The development of the design program for any project must be guided by the engineers' understanding of the marketplace and the needs of the homebuyers of the target market. The goal of meeting the design program should outweigh the need for innovation. Engineers need to incorporate emotion into their designs. As an example in retirement community design, special attention must be made to the design and land planning for amenities, which usually include pools, clubhouses, tennis courts, special entrance features, security measures, walking trails, and other features that help the homebuyer feel comfortable in the new surroundings. Sensitive land planning and emotional engineering bring a project to life with the specific intent to create a living environment that will sell out quickly.

The design approach taken for a specific market should be pursued for all specific market segments. This will increase the marketability of a project and make the engineering community sensitive to the needs of the consumer. Engineers need to look beyond the right-of-way line, and each home on a lot should be a project, designed for the ultimate user in mind.

LOCATION

It is true that *location, location, location* is the key element of a project that cannot be remedied by money. In site analysis work, location is simply the starting point for the selection of the property. It is also the end point when the project is open for sale. Not only is *location, location, location* important for the marketability of the project, but it is important for the regulatory approval and cost of the project. Connecting to existing infrastructure (i.e., perimeter roads, existing water or sewer lines, or existing drainage facilities) is important to the overall cost of developing the land. However, location goes beyond pure cost.

Buyers are seeking subdivisions and housing communities that are well located and close to public services, public offices, shopping centers, and other amenities that add to the quality of life and convenience of everyday living.

Engineers providing site selection and analysis services must concentrate on property location and the site characteristics to enhance the marketability of the site. In terms of analyzing property for purchase deliberation and development purposes, location should be the primary factor in assessing the advantages of introducing a new project in the marketplace.

In-fill properties previously overlooked may yield greater benefits. Overlooked properties have a problem. Engineers can investigate the problems and prepare creative solutions to overcome the problem. The land should be purchased with the knowledge of the constraints and thus should be purchased under market price. Engineers can add value to the overlooked parcels by designing creatively to further enhance the marketability of the project. It is much more advantageous to find niche markets that can be satisfied with overlooked in-fill properties because the land values should be below market price.

COMPETITION

It is a good practice for builders to have a new project close to the competition. The traffic generated from a competitor's print media, radio advertisements, and direct mail campaigns will attract buyers to their projects and will spill over to adjacent or nearby projects. The idea of differentiating your project from your competitors, once the buyers visit your site, is an important ingredient of success. The differences can be in materials, product, color, presentation, or orientation price but more importantly in a street scene that emanates a comfort zone.

If your project is better located, better priced, and of better value, being close to the competition will result in higher absorption rates and ultimately a more profitable project. The selection of an in-fill site over a rural setting may be an excellent decision for your marketplace.

LAND PLAN

The pricing structure for builders does not vary significantly. Large regional builders may have some benefit in their buying power, but their subdivision design will not necessarily be more creative. The pricing of homes or lots directly correlates with the subdivision design and the perceived value created by a creative land plan. The sales price of a home does not have a direct relationship with the cost of building the project. The market sets the price of the home or lot and hopefully the builder/developer will realize a profit on the land and an additional percentage on the house, lot premiums, and extras. Proper land planning for the marketplace and the selection of the hot button amenities for enhancing the site features will increase the perceived value of the project and not necessarily add to the overall cost. This reinforces the need to present an imaginative land plan and prepare a conceptual cost estimate before the purchase of the property. The highest and best use of the discretionary funds should be determined at the conceptual land planning phase.

The land planning techniques resulting in high lot yields, creative open spaces, and environmentally sensitive land consumption will be more readily accepted by the public, making it easier to market the project.

However, new housing ideas in an area may not be readily accepted by the homebuying public. Builders want to be leaders but not pioneers in a marketplace. They will not introduce zero lot line or small single-family lots in a marketplace when 0.5-acre lots are the norm, unless, of course, the market research indicates a need for a lower price point and the government promotes smaller lots. Builders would then seriously consider the idea as long as the market potential and depth existed for this approach. As an engineer, it is important to illustrate to your clients your understanding of the marketplace and the creative land planning approaches that can be successfully implemented in your marketplace. New land planning ideas are a result of the land characteristics and the housing product selected. In most markets, a typical subdivision with open spaces will succeed because that is what the homebuying public perceives as a quality subdivision. It will succeed also because most local government standards are not flexible enough to allow innovation in land planning. Without question, the larger the project size, the easier it is to maximize the number of units and be able to afford the ambiance of a creative subdivision design.

LOT PREMIUMS

When the housing market is thriving, builders will slow down the absorption rate for the more marketable lots. All buyers would want the best location, Especially if the best lots had views, woods, and privacy or were located at the end of a cul-de-sac. To slow down the sale of the best lots, the builder can either hold the lots off the market, which is a negative approach, or place lot premiums on the lots.

This would slow down the selection of the best lots and allow the typical lots to be sold and constructed first. The philosophy is that the best lots will always sell.

Land plans create lots that can be marketed with lot premiums. These lots will have unique characteristics and are distinctly different from the typical subdivision lots. Engineers should be analyzing each individual lot within the project to ensure the building footprint is consistent with the builder's house line and to provide flexibility to sell any of the homes on each lot, which would permit a builder to file for a prototype building permit.

Cul-de-sac roads and lots provide an excellent location for homebuyers. Cul-de-sacs are always the first lots to be sold even with lot premiums. These lots provide a sense of privacy, security, and safety for the homeowners. In most instances, the elimination of through traffic within a subdivision will be beneficial to the overall presentation of the project to the homebuying public.

There seems to be a trend that regulatory planners want to reduce or eliminate cul-de-sacs. Their opinion is that connectivity, which involves connecting streets rather than terminating streets in a cul-de-sac, is more desirable. Their goal is to legislate the interaction between homeowners and prevent isolation of a group of homeowners at the end of a cul-de-sac. This thought process is a serious miscalculation of the marketplace. This approach is one more misguided planning concept that is implemented for cars and municipal vehicles rather than for the homebuyers. In fact, all market segments from the first-time homebuyer to the retirement buyer prefer cul-de-sac lots. In fact, the elimination of a cul-de-sac bulb would be a practical design change for the limited number of lots the street would serve. The design community should not waiver from the needs of the marketplace. If so, this land plan would result in higher lot costs and slower absorption rates.

Engineers must land plan for a maximum number of premium lots by using the land characteristics and land constraints to determine the ultimate marketability of the project. Most builders do not include lot premiums in their pro forma. However, premium lots add to the success equation.

HOUSING SELECTION

Engineers should know what type and style of houses are selling in their marketplace. They should even walk through competitors' models to view the presentation inside and outside of the house. The engineer must not stop at the front walk. The construction techniques used by builders in the marketplace are also important to understand. An engineer can enhance client relations and design a better-quality subdivision by understanding how the building industry functions and markets their product.

The foundation selection is a function of the marketplace but should also be a function of the characteristics of the land. An engineer must be the advocate of the land and how the land can add value and increase absorption by ensuring that housing selection and foundations are designed both for the land and the consumer.

Many builders will follow the marketplace and offer product selections that are similar in the size and style of other builders. To show differentiation, a builder will change the product specifications inside the house. In a "hot" market, this may be the only marketing change that needs to occur. However, in a slow market, this change would not be enough. Thus, the engineer must add the perceived value into the subdivision design and land plan all the time. All too often, we choose not to remember a down-market scenario. There are time valued planning and design concepts that add perceived value to any subdivision regardless of the marketplace or market.

House and site landscaping, gated communities, entry features, design emphasis on people rather than cars, lot orientation, privacy, and maintenance considerations are all important subdivision design ingredients all the time.

There are situations in which preplanning the house type for each lot becomes necessary; for example, foundations should be constructed in the late fall for winter housing production. Preplanning does not allow consumers flexibility in the selection of the home or lot, but the builder will know the costs and increase efficiency in production. Salespersons will balk at the idea of preplanning. Engineers must recognize when the need for preplanning exists and learn the phasing requirements for each project. The phasing of the number of lots released for sale and the cost of the infrastructure are important all the time. Design the subdivision so that your builder/developer limits the cashflow, increases marketing flexibility, and can stop the project at well-defined stages. If the builder chooses not to stop at the phase lines and continues the infrastructure improvements to meet the market demand, then the builder's confidence level is high and an increase in sales abortion must be realized to stay in line with the infrastructure improvements. However, the decision of the builder should not affect the way the engineer designs the subdivision infrastructure.

Engineers need to have a keen understanding of the *actual* cost of developing property and the cost ramifications of the subdivision design features. Engineers need to go beyond the road right-of-way in their design approach and their understanding of the marketplace.

MARKETING APPROACH

In most markets, a model home is required for buyers to consider before they buy. A model home presents confidence that the project is "real." The quality of the products, construction, and presentation provide first and lasting impressions that will make or break a project.

Engineers need to completely understand the motive and intent of models and model home complexes. The selection of the proper model home location must address the following:

1. The cost to install the infrastructure to serve the models
2. The timing of the model center construction to commence as soon as possible
3. The orientation of the homes on the lots
   a. For curb appeal—the way consumers will view the house when they first drive up to the model center
   b. The view outside from inside of the model—What will consumers see from all of the window locations?
   c. The natural light inside of the house during the entire day
4. The sales trap within the model center—Have homebuyers visit the models by coming into and out of the sales area.
5. The arrangement of the model homes in terms of pricing—Start with the standard home and walk to the largest model, which offers increased sales and perceived values.
6. Design of the model center to enhance excitement in the buying process
7. Creation of a sense of urgency
8. Landscape, hardscape, walkways, lighting, and signage considerations

The model center and model homes set the tone for the project and the acceptance of the project by the marketplace. The engineer needs to incorporate the model center ideas early in the land planning phase of design. It is also appropriate for the engineer to become involved in the model center beyond the normal grading, drainage, and utility design elements.

Other elements of the marketing approach for a project include sign locations, entrance features, and other ideas that give the project a sense of identity and a memory point of reference for the homebuyers. Engineers should consider different paving materials at entrances, even for public roadways, to provide a sense of arrival to the project. The successful engineering firm in the residential industry thinks like a builder/developer and becomes a leader in the project design team.

SUBDIVISION POTENTIAL

During the site analysis phase, the engineer should investigate the development potential of adjacent properties. It would make sense for a builder to continue building operations in the same location. The subdivision design should accommodate future infrastructure extensions to adjacent properties. Engineers have a positive effect on the market's acceptance of the project. Through flexible land planning and engineering design, the engineer controls the cost of development, affects the marketability of the lots, and establishes a sense of community within the project. Understanding the residential marketing strategies of the building industry will assist the engineer in better serving the client base and in creating memorable subdivision designs.

CHAPTER 5

Consultants

ROLE OF CONSULTANTS

Each design professional involved in the subdivision process can contribute to a better living environment for future homeowners. Attention should be given to ensure that the design criteria's relevance to housing projects is primary—not for commercial, industrial, or highway design purposes. Design professionals do not receive educational training to design residential subdivisions.

The design professional, regardless of discipline, learns how to design residential subdivisions through experience and experience alone. Subdivisions are designed by professionals, who use what they have learned from past bad experiences to help shape their design approaches in subsequent housing projects.

The physical attributes of a site provide the framework for creative design approaches and patterns that make each housing project unique. The proper use of the land will, over time and after many projects, establish the reputation of the developer and design team. Successful housing design professionals are sensitive to site characteristics and how to use the land to benefit the eventual user.

Talented design professionals may work out of their garage or basement or be on staff at the largest regional design firm. The design professional best suited for designing a subdivision is the person who understands the factors controlling the housing development process. In the selection of a design professional, start with an investigation at the planning and zoning office to determine the designers used by the competition.

Keep in mind that just because these firms are doing work in the community does not guarantee that their work is of good quality. Review project plans at the planning office and compare the approach with the constructed subdivision. Determine if the project was constructed consistently with the plans. Also, make a determination if the design firm is well received at the planning office. Reputable firms with qualified personnel are necessary ingredients in obtaining per-

Photo 5-1. Project Goals. The architectural, planning, and engineering design characteristics of a subdivision should blend together to create a housing subdivision meeting the needs of the homeowner.

mits and approvals in a timely manner. Their ability to understand the political and governmental influence on housing will help shorten the approval process.

Residential subdivision design work requires a unique talent found in regional engineering, planning, and architectural firms. This design talent must be sensitive to the way people intend to live. The subdivision design must be able to compete in the marketplace. The difference between large, local, or even regional firms and the cottage industry professional is not their design abilities but the overhead costs of providing the design service.

SELECTION PROCESS

The following criteria should be used as a guide in the selection process of the design team:

1. *Cooperation.* Does the consultant have the ability to use ideas generated through project discussions and implement those ideas with enthusiasm?
2. *Knowledge.* Does the consultant have specific knowledge to prepare a design consistent with the design intent of the project?
3. *Manpower.* Does the firm have sufficient manpower to handle their current workload and manage the proposed project? The project should receive the

same attention as any other similar project. Any less attention would indicate a manpower problem.

4. *Experience.* Evaluate the educational background and work experience of the personnel assigned to the project. Visit existing projects designed by the consultant. Is the project appealing? Do the homes complement the land form?

5. *Commitment.* During the discussions with the design team, will the consultant make a commitment to adhere to the project schedule? A personal commitment to a project schedule is important in having the regulatory submissions made on time.

6. *Fees.* The fee and negotiated contract provisions should reflect a lump sum for specific scopes of work. Does this approach define the work and identify all of the costs expected during the design and regulatory process?

The contract agreement with the design professional should be based on a specific time frame for the plans to be completed and submitted to the regulatory agency. To be used as a guideline, Figure 5-1 is a professional service agreement used for various design professionals retained for housing projects. Not all design professionals will be used for every housing project. For a single-family traditional housing project, the following disciplines should be considered for the design team: civil engineer, environmentalist, architect, landscape designer, surveyor, and soils engineer. Other professionals to be considered would be an economist, to determine the effect of the project on municipal services, schools, fire, and first aid capabilities; a traffic engineer, to determine the effect the project would have on existing roadway systems; and a planner, to prepare the conceptual site plan. If managed properly, the land planner, who determines the highest and best use of the land, can be the most cost-effective professional retained by a developer.

DESIGN TEAM MEMBERS

The success of a housing project is measured by the ability of the project design team to obtain governmental approvals and permits in a time frame consistent with company objectives. Ask each design professional to commit to a production schedule for the project. The following outlines the work responsibilities for each design professional and can be used as a guide when discussing work scopes.

Surveyor

The surveyor will provide, at the very beginning of every project, a boundary survey, which would include researching deeds to investigate all easements and encumbrances affecting that property. The survey should include and detail the existing infrastructure in and around the project site, such as roadways, existing drainage facilities, telephone poles, fire hydrants, other utilities, and other existing structures that could affect the ultimate layout of the property. In addition to

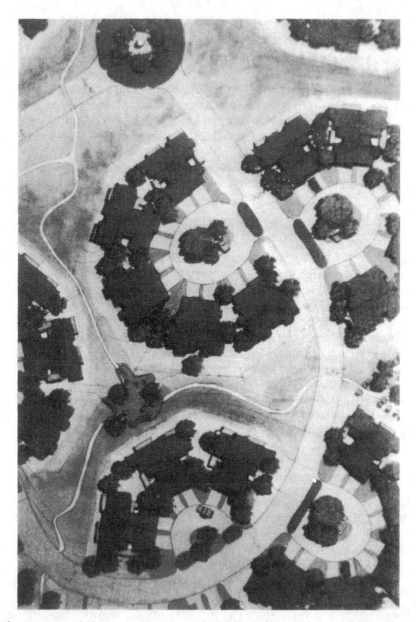

Photo 5-2. Land Planning. Organize a design team having the expertise and talent necessary to prepare a land plan that meets the marketing goals of the project. Design team members should complement each other and the results will be well received by the marketplace.

the boundary survey, a complete topography survey is required. The topography is obtained by aerial photography or by an actual field survey. If possible, consider paying for low-flying aerial photography to ensure an accurate topographical survey. The boundary and topography surveys are essential elements of the base map used for land planning.

Environmental Consultant

The environmental consultant site inspection scope of work will vary from project to project and from one state to another. The Corps of Engineers are charged with the federal responsibility for wetland protection. Some states have expanded their role in the protection of wetland areas. The environmental consultant would walk the site, take necessary soil borings, inspect and identify vegetation, analyze the soil, and determine the depth of the groundwater to ascertain the presence of wetland areas. These areas would be flagged in the field and be ready for the surveyor to delineate the wetland line by metes and bounds for incorporation in the base map. The environmental consultant should have knowledge of endangered species and endangered vegetation that are protected by federal, state, and local laws. Other environmental restrictions that should be reviewed and included in the final report are archeological areas, recreation requirements, the type and size of significant trees and stressed vegetation found on the site, flood plains, etc. A list of the soils affecting the ability to develop the project should be incorporated into the final environmental report.

Soil Scientist

The soil consultant manages soil testing rigs and the apparatus used to dig test pits and to undertake a soil boring program for each site under consideration. This investigative work will validate characteristics of the site and correlate the data with the soil conservation district soils map. The information provided in the soils report would include the following:

1. Definition of the soils onsite
2. Capability of the soil to be used for structural fill, foundation work, road construction, and septic systems
3. Analysis of the topsoil
4. Location of unsuitable material required to be supplemented with other types of material
5. Identification of the groundwater elevation and determination if the installation of utilities would require dewatering, resulting in added expense to the project

For residential subdivisions, a grid-patterned soil analysis program is not always necessary. In fact, in many cases, it would be a waste of time and effort to provide testing of areas located in open spaces or on the lots where buildings would not be located, that is, setback areas or buffers. Thus, the program should concentrate on the center portions of the site where the significant housing and roadway activities will occur. The soil scientist would be able to outline a program for identifying the soil onsite and provide recommendations on the benefits and use of the site soils. In areas of rock, low areas, and unsuitable soils, the soil testing program should be expanded to ensure the site is fully analyzed. The soil testing results should be discussed with the land development contractor. Removing the soil unknowns from land development contract negotiations further enhances the ability to accurately predict costs.

Land Planner

This discipline, in some states, is for a registered and licensed professional. However, in most instances, the land planner is the architect, landscape architect, or engineer for the project. The skill of the land planner is effectively used in the public sector for master planning of communities, zoning maps, and planning capital improvement projects. However, the land planning discipline can consolidate all of the design intents in preparing a subdivision land plan that adheres to all bulk requirements of the zone. All design issues need to be addressed before the submission of the design plans. Limit or eliminate variances or design waivers to minimize the political scrutiny of the project.

In ascertaining subdivision improvement costs and adherence to market conditions, several planning schemes may be required to arrive at the plan that meets company goals. Land planning for residential subdivisions can be mastered by the builder/developer or given to a land planner at minimum cost. A concept plan prepared in-house would help company executives understand the land potential before retaining the land planner.

The land planner's goal is to maximize the density and adhere to the highest and best use for the property while achieving high project marketability. Ask the land planner to prepare a loose conceptual lot and street layout, which would be subsequently revised to meet all the technical requirements imposed by local government. If a land planner is retained to prepare site plans, do not restrict their creativity. New, fresh planning ideas can provide a marketing edge. The land planner will also lay out the basic elements of the project site, that is, road alignments, lot configurations, open spaces, walkways, and tree-save areas. The other design professionals accept the land plan and modify the concept to meet the technical requirements of the municipality.

Engineer

This discipline is the primary designer of subdivisions. The engineer takes all of the conceptual drawings and uses residential design criteria to prepare the subdivision design. The lot layout and street rights-of-way will be hardlined on the conceptual plan. The subdivision infrastructure is designed by an engineering design professional registered in the state in which they practice. The engineer assigned to the project needs to be a registered engineer and not an engineer in

Photo 5-3. Implementation. The project design plans will meet the project marketing goals only if the implementation in the field is consistent with the design documents.

training. Request to have an engineer with housing experience assigned to the project. Review their work before hiring them.

The engineer's role is to design vertical and horizontal alignments of the internal roadways; design access points onto existing roadways; design water, sewer, and drainage systems for the project; and design the grading of each lot. The proper engineering approach should:

1. Minimize design variances from regulatory criteria
2. Minimize unusual construction costs
3. Minimize complex engineering design to maximize quality control
4. Minimize awkward lot layouts to maximize land values for marketing success

Landscape Architect

This design discipline can provide significant insight on the full utilization of the existing attributes of a site. The landscape architect provides information on tree-save areas and identifies specimen trees that should be saved. This design approach will save on clearing costs and establish lot premiums for lots containing such vegetation. Landscape architects can also provide design input on irrigation systems, project identification features, street tree planting, housing landscape packages, color coordination, product orientation, and selection of ground cover and grasses. The landscape architect's contribution to a housing project is to visualize the street scene and to field-manage the design intent to ensure the site features are accentuated.

Architect

A competent housing architect can use the land plan and marketing information to provide a design development program that produces sales consistent with the competition's absorption rates. The architect should be consulted on the selection of the standard foundation style of each house, that is, walkout basements, in-ground basements, front-to-back or side-to-side split levels, crawl spaces, etc. The engineer will use this information for site grading purposes. The architect will use the site analysis report to prepare housing plans, which use the ground, views, and topography to the benefit of the buyer of the lot or the homebuyer. The sales price range of the product line will dictate the budget for houseline construction. The architect should use this financial constraint to ensure the designs are marketable and can be constructed within budget.

Other Disciplines

A fiscal analysis of a project site and its economic effect on schools, emergency services, fire departments, etc., may be necessary and can be prepared by an economist or a land planner. They should have knowledge of the municipal services and the school system of the community. Their analysis should illustrate that

Photo 5-4. Consultants. The role of the design consultant is to provide creative ideas and concepts using the physical attributes of the site. Creativity in land planning and infrastructure design should be cost-effective innovation.

the new homes would generate more new taxes than the cost of the community services to serve the homes. A real estate agent could provide testimony and background on housing prices and verification of the market study. Interior designers would provide input on color schemes, architectural layouts, project identification features, marketing schemes, and model decorating. Attorneys are key project members during the land purchase and governmental permitting processes. The complexities of real estate law should require legal representation for each project. Retaining the services of a local attorney is a prudent business decision to ensure corporate and personal protection under local, state, and federal laws.

The use of any consultant should be evaluated on the basis of need for each particular project. Do not hesitate to hire a consultant who will have a positive influence on the approval, construction, sale, or closing of a project. The minimum number of consultants needed on any housing project would be the surveyor and engineer. The other disciplines could be retained and used, as required, before and during the regulatory process. As with any consultant, communicate the project objectives, outline the expectations, and seek a commitment to a schedule. All consultants retained should be sensitive to the social environment of the subdivision, its functionality, livability, and longevity. The consultant is a tool of success in the housing industry. Use and manage this tool to attain market acceptability of the subdivision and product.

PROFESSIONAL SERVICE AGREEMENT

The professional service agreement for consultants is provided in Figure 5-1. This agreement is a base contract agreement between the builder/developer and any design professional. The general provisions of this agreement are common provisions for all consultants and for any project. Once executed by a consultant, specific project contracts can refer back to this base agreement for general provisions such as:

1. Ownership of plans
2. Compliance with regulations imposed by local, regional, state, and federal governments
3. Indemnification clause
4. Professional liability and errors and omissions insurance policies (An insurance certificate must be submitted to the owner and kept on file for reference.)
5. Termination clause for both the builder/developer and the design professional

For specific projects, use the general contract language and scope of work descriptions outlined in Figures 5-2 through 5-5. These contracts are for site feasibility and surveying, land planning, engineering, and architecture. This basic information will provide builder/developers with a basis for negotiating contractual agreements with design professionals. The scope of work can be modified to meet the needs and requirements of each specific site and project.

A detailed description of the surveying scope of work required to prepare a subdivision plat for recordation purposes is outlined in Figure 5-6. This description of services includes the boundary and topographic surveys. The scopes of work outline the requirements for the surveyor to record the final plat, establish field controls, provide land development construction layout, and provide houseline surveying. Figure 5-7 is a detailed scope of services for housing construction surveying.

The architectural services should complement the engineering work and regulatory process. The architectural services include design development work to establish the design program and housing product for the project. Once completed, the preliminary design phases and final construction documents would be prepared in accordance with the scope of work.

The construction documents need to be signed and sealed by a registered architect. This should be requested of the architect if required by the building department or for the builder's own use. The signing and sealing of construction documents establishes the liability of the construction documents and elevates the importance of the documents in the field. Some states do not require a licensed architect to prepare one- and two-family residential construction plans. Some states require certified designers to prepare the plans for building permit purposes.

CONSULTANT RESPONSIBILITY

If a consultant is retained for design services, the builder/developer should use the contract agreement to ensure the construction documents are consistent with all governmental regulations and are of sufficient detail to obtain building permits. The purpose of using design consultants knowledgeable in residential housing construction is for the preparation of plans sensitive to the ultimate user and for the obtaining of regulatory permits in a much more efficient manner.

Once the project is under construction, the plans should not be open for interpretation. There will always be construction variations, construction mistakes, or design changes that should be approved by the design professional. All deviations from the plans should be approved by the design professional to ensure their professional liability does not become null and void. The contract documents prepared become the basis not only for all bid considerations and cost estimates, but for the future selection of design professionals. The guideline for assessing the ability of the land development contractor and the success of the project are the construction documents.

Because design professionals should sign, seal, and stand behind their design approach, it is convenient for consultants to use governmental regulations to justify the design approach. However, in all instances, it is incumbent on the design professional to use those regulations in a framework that best benefits the project as a whole. If the project schedule is managed properly and the closing schedule is not jeopardized, the designer may propose to use standards that are in conflict with regulatory standards but that enhance the project's approach, aesthetic appearance, and function.

Design professionals must balance the special interests of the project, including the government, the client, the demands of producing a subdivision meeting the market, and their own professional ethics and design philosophies for residential projects. The successful designer is one who balances all of these considerations into an approach that can be efficiently approved, effectively marketed, and satisfactorily constructed.

Design professionals must be advocates of the homebuying public, who is not present, to support the new housing project at regulatory hearings. The professional housing designer uses the market information and prepares a subdivision that complements and uses government regulations as guidelines to ultimately meet the needs of the new homebuyer. Because consultants are in the business to earn a living, the design professional needs to complete a project so that another project can then be added to the workload. The greater the workload or number of projects, the more the potential for financial success is possible. Housing projects require attention to detail that can be lost when a consultant strives to finish one project in order to start another.

It is important for builders and developers to assess the capabilities of design professionals to ensure that their project is receiving proper staff attention. Builder/developers should obtain the highest priority from the design consultant. Design professionals must be held to a very high standard in preparing construction documents for residential housing projects. Once the project is being constructed or has been completed, it is the reputation of the builder/developer that is evaluated by government and the general public—not the consultant or the land development contractor.

CHAPTER 6

Land Planning Concepts

The residential building industry, over many years, has progressed in the use of land and in the development of planning concepts. Although many communities vary their zoning districts to change the densities, land planning approaches have not changed dramatically over the years. The land planning concepts of many communities started with the pattern found in many older towns and cities. Neighborhoods in which homes were close to the roadway and close to neighbors formed a sense of community and a sense of belonging. Duplicating these concepts is difficult, if not impossible. The bulk requirements imposed by local government stifle creativity and ingenuity, and land development standards cause most creative approaches to be less than cost effective.

Creating a sense of community within a residential community can be achieved if the project is of sufficient size to effectively and financially create a lifestyle the market can embrace. The larger the parcel of land and the greater the number of housing units within a commercial/industrial component, the greater flexibility in creating a land plan unique to the property and to the marketplace. However, not every community embraces new land planning approaches, nor can developers amass sufficient land holdings to create a new community. Also, many developers do not want to take the chance on a new land planning concept because of the risk of government and market rejection of the idea. Thus, local governments have instituted land planning approaches in the zoning ordinance to guide development patterns. These regulatory design approaches are legislating the way people should live without regard to how the people want to live.

The market dictates the sales price of a home. The zoning dictates the number of homes, and the land dictates the success of the project. After each peak in a housing cycle, the building industry always faces local governmental and resident efforts to stifle continued residential growth. In fact, many jurisdictions downzone properties to achieve less dense projects. Local government should, however, be assessing land availability, existing infrastructure, and density factors to encourage in-fill or smart growth patterns rather than encourage suburbanization of a community.

AFFORDABLE HOMES

When local governments institute regulations on land use that impede growth or financial profitability, the building community must seek out fringe and suburban areas to meet the demands of the marketplace. It is the suburban properties that meet the market demands with larger lots for bigger homes. This planning approach will significantly affect the way our communities are developed for years to come. Exhausting our land resources through low-density development and overextending community infrastructure to service these developments will halt housing development in many parts of the country.

The affordability gap in the housing market continues to widen. The lack of affordable housing is an acute problem for many communities, and a combined regulatory, builder, and engineering approach to development is necessary to bridge this gap. To achieve affordability, builders need flexibility in the way land is used and in the standards that regulate how the land is developed. The price of land does not reflect the marketability or acceptability of the housing product. Land designated with higher densities allows builders to spread the cost of development, land, and land development over more units, thus permitting builders to reach the first-time homebuying market and reduce the affordability gap.

LAND PLANNING FOR MARKETABILITY

Within many housing markets, the competition for homebuyers is always keen. A housing project distinguishes itself from its competition with the design of the home and the land planning approach for the project. The design of the home can easily be offset by another builder with price adjustments or product enhancements, but the site characteristics and infrastructure planning cannot significantly be adjusted after approvals and permits. Significant tree-save areas within a subdivision enhance the ambiance of the street scene.

Land planning for marketability is not a new concept. The creativity of the land plan, the site amenities, the street scene, the aesthetic presentation, and environmental considerations are all ingredients of a successful housing project. These elements will create the sense of community all buyers seek and will set the project apart from the competition. A well thought out and visualized land plan with attractive street scenes combined with useable, livable, and properly oriented lots will increase absorption rates and the perceived value of the homes.

Engineers should be elevating their land planning and subdivision design skills to the next level of attention. A housing project need not be designed in a vacuum, and each lot should be considered an individual project. Proper grading, orientation of the house, varying setbacks, landscaping, and lot usability are key elements to the marketability of the lots and project. Engineers should pay special attention to the location of driveways, the location of garages, and the lot topography to maintain existing natural features of the lot. The less grading and clearing on a lot, the better the product is received by the homebuying public.

There are valid reasons to incorporate different land planning concepts in the marketplace to present a clear choice. Many new land planning concepts are not embraced by the public and the regulators. Most locales have their own approaches as to how land is developed, and bulk requirements vary from one location to the next. Many municipalities try to legislate how to use land for housing developments. Regulators strive to legislate how projects are developed and how people will live in these projects. Unfortunately, this legislative approach is not market sensitive, and many projects do not move forward because builders are unwilling to try something new in the marketplace. Residential land planning has everything to do with the desires of the marketplace. The density, style of home, and size of project become secondary to the planning approach.

Land prices match the demand but very rarely depreciate. Thus, builders must raise house prices, achieve higher densities, or seek outlying areas with lower land prices. Because builders can't continue to raise prices and government controls the density, builders are seeking fringe or suburban areas to continue their building programs. This has caused a reaction from many municipalities and their citizens to slow or curb housing development. Knowing that land prices do not substantially depreciate in a slow economy, the pent-up market demanding housing will travel to outlying areas for the housing. This stresses infrastructure, adds to transportation costs, and causes government to down-zone property. There are many examples of slow growth movements. The approach should be to find ways to concentrate growth in areas where the government considers housing a must and to manage the existing infrastructure to match the development patterns.

HIGH-DENSITY DEVELOPMENTS

Most zoning approaches earmark high-density developments close to other non-residential uses, existing infrastructure, and difficult sites. Land planning concepts for higher-density projects are governed by the housing type accepted by the marketplace. In many locales, zero lot line or small lot single-family subdivisions are not well received or only well received by a segment of the marketplace (i.e., retirement housing). New land planning approaches for high-density projects concentrate on the amenities of the project, the views, and the open-space planning. The flexibility in road or parking lot design dictates how many projects are developed. Engineers should concentrate on how the housing units relate to each other and plan the infrastructure around the housing orientations and not the other way around. Higher-density developments such as zero lot line, small single-family lots; patio homes; duplexes; fourplexes; townhouses; and low-, mid-, and highrises will be limited by many jurisdictions in order to control growth. This is exactly the wrong approach to establishing sensible growth patterns and meeting the pent-up demand for affordable housing. Higher density will give builders a better opportunity to offer affordable housing prices to first-time home-buyers.

CLUSTER ZONING

Cluster zoning is being implemented by many jurisdictions with the goal of increasing open-space developments. In essence, a cluster zoning deed restricts a portion of the project and consolidates the housing in one location, generally on smaller lots to achieve the density permitted within the gross acreage of the site. This approach has an obvious benefit to the taxpaying community by limiting infrastructure maintenance and the cost of community services. The problem that exists with this land use option is that the homebuying public may not want smaller single-family lots—even if the homes are of comparable size and style to those in larger lot developments. It is clear that the marketplace is demanding larger homes on larger lots. Cluster zoning is a tool that can be successful in the correct circumstance. The site also will have a bearing on the success of cluster land planning. Cluster zoning should not be a zone within a municipality but rather a flexible planning option permitted in all zones. Although this planning approach is not new, cluster provisions are not widely used because builders are hesitant to try this planning approach without really predicting the market acceptance.

NEOTRADITIONAL

This land planning concept is an attempt to replicate the community design approaches of the traditional urban planning concepts of de-emphasizing garages and cars while emphasizing the humanization of a project. Today's neotraditional approach has the same elements and street scenes of older communities. This is a much more pedestrian-friendly planning approach with smaller streets, street trees, small lot frontages, close front setbacks, and garages tucked in the back-yard. The concept is valid and can be quite successful in the correct environment. The garages can connect to alleyways in the backs of the lots while the homes face the residential streets. Builders will attempt this land planning concept if the regulations governing the street and alleyway design are modified and are flexi-ble in the standards governing the infrastructure design. The land development cost for neotraditional plans will be higher, but it can be offset by a higher density associated with this type of development. Even if the regulations are flexible and the density factors advantageous, builders will try this approach only if it pro-vides a competitive edge in the marketplace and if the market is ready for the design approach.

RETIREMENT HOUSING

Creative land planning approaches to retirement community design are tantamount to a successful project. In many communities, the retirement market is only starting to emerge. Engineers need to understand and appreciate the retirement market and those elements of the community design that are necessary for a project to succeed. There are different levels of retirement community design based on the age group and services required to serve that group. This market segment will only increase as the baby boomers age. Serving this market segment with new housing and alternative housing concepts will generate new approaches to land planning ideas and regulatory control. It will also cause the existing housing stock to turn over in home ownership and bridge the affordability gap in many communities. The engineer needs to understand the needs and desires of the retirement market. If they have the land planning skills, expertise, and creativity for this market segment, their client base will expand by word of mouth.

CONNECTIVITY

A new land planning concept has been accepted in many municipalities, directing the way people will interact and live. Connectivity is the linkage of roads within a project and the elimination of cul-de-sacs. Regulatory planners are seeking social interconnections within a housing project, because their goal is to enhance social good and recreate the urban environment of the housing project. The advocation of eliminating cul-de-sacs by providing interconnection between streets is contrary to the way people want to live. Most homebuyers prefer to live on cul-de-sacs or short streets with limited traffic. Not only are the conflicts between vehicles and pedestrians minimized, the homeowners consider the design safer and secure.

PARTNERSHIPS IN PLANNING

Housing professionals and the regulatory community should partner to develop design alternatives that are market driven rather than imposed by regulation. Legislating social economic values on the homebuying public falls short of its goal in implementing new land planning concepts. In some cases, the increased cost of development and market rejection of a housing concept is the real ramification of a failed planning concept.

State and local planning officials are reacting to the strong housing market by smart growth initiatives that will direct housing projects toward sites with existing infrastructure. The problem with this approach is that the cost of land is generally higher in value with existing infrastructure in place. The raw land commodity is the one factor that cannot be controlled. The need for someone to sell land is primarily an economic decision. Builders will purchase land at a premium only if the market can absorb the higher housing prices. If the market demand is for a lower sales price, the builder will seek fringe, suburban, or in-fill properties with higher densities to offset the cost of land. Land values do not always follow the supply and demand curves or remain consistent with historical sales prices. The other reaction by the government to overdevelopment is to down-zone properties. As a result of this action, land values increase on a per-unit basis and home prices are driven higher. Again, the gap in affordable housing widens as the government reacts to housing growth.

A partnership among engineers, builders, and government officials is important in developing a true smart growth initiative that properly builds on existing infrastructure and meets the needs of the various housing markets. New land planning concepts and approaches will stem from these initiatives. Every community has its own unique housing demands, and housing solutions should be a result of consensus among the various groups involved in the design, approval, and construction of homes. Engineers have an opportunity to be key participants in the housing of Americans. Engineers need to take an active local role in the development of housing ideas, concepts, and programs.

CHAPTER 7

Conceptual Design Planning

The conceptual land planning phase of a project has always been the most important aspect of project development. This phase establishes the foundation for the entire project design. This phase also determines the ultimate cost of the project. The conceptual designing is the creative part of the land development process. This creativity, however, has to be tempered with the knowledge of financial limitations and of the housing product to be marketed on the site. Just because a land plan has been prepared and contains the fine attributes of a community design, the developer must ask, "Can the project be built to sell homes or lots and make a profit?"

Builder/developers should hire consultants for the land planning phase because the value received will far exceed the cost of the consulting services. The cost associated in preparing alternative land plans to evaluate gross lot yields and land development costs is a prudent business expenditure. This land planning approach should be considered before the purchase of land for development purposes. The conceptual land plan can be used for negotiation purposes with a seller by determining the ultimate lot yield of a site. The lot yield is the ultimate indicator of the land value.

BASE MAP

A boundary survey is necessary to create the base map used for land planning purposes.

Figure 7-1 is a detailed checklist for the elements of a boundary survey. To ensure the survey is complete, review the plan prepared by the surveyor and easily check off those items on this list that appear on the plan. The base map must contain all of this information to undertake a meaningful land plan. Figure 7-2 is a checklist for the topographic survey work, which, combined with the boundary survey, will provide a complete base map used for land planning purposes. The

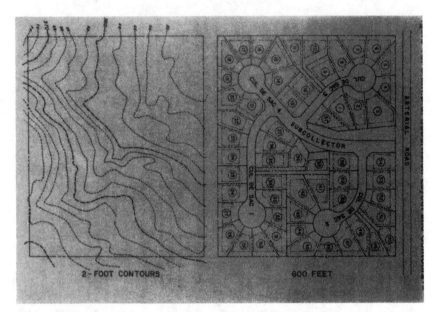

Photo 7-1. Base Map. An accurate topographic and boundary survey is required for the preparation of a project base map. The base map will be used by the design team in developing the project land plan.

topographic information can be obtained through aerial photography. On sites of 10 acres or less, a field topographic survey can be done to produce a more accurate base map for the project site. In preparing a design program for a residential project, determine the architectural product and the highest and best use of the land. Elements of the land plan and lot layout should be consistent with the design program.

ELEMENTS OF A CONCEPTUAL LAND PLAN

The base plan is prepared by a surveyor and includes the boundary and topographic survey information. The land planner will analyze the site conditions and constraints affecting the use of the land and will ultimately determine the lot yield. The base plan should show the existing frontage road and elevations. This information is required to determine the best intersection location with the perimeter roadway. The proposed access location should be evaluated against the existing site constraints, such as telephone poles, fire hydrants, etc. Select the location of the road access to eliminate any conflict with existing facilities. The vertical and horizontal site distance requirements at the proposed intersection should be evaluated. As an example, the access to the site should not be located on a horizontal or vertical curve that restricts the site distance at the intersection.

Project costs would increase if the offsite roadway needed to be improved as a result of the project.

Topography

Review the information on the base map. The closer together the topographic lines, the steeper the slope. The typical slope for residential streets and/or driveways is no greater than 10% grade. Grades of 10% or greater would require a special housing design approach in order to use the existing site topography. Steep slopes may cause excessive cuts and fills that would increase the cost of land development. A wider distance between topographic lines would indicate a flatter slope. Thus, by reviewing a topography plan, it is easy to determine the undulations of the site and determine if the site would require special engineering skills to maximize lot yield and minimize land development costs.

Drainage

Any natural drainage swales or channels within the site must be clearly shown on the base map. Natural drainage courses are depicted by topographic lines that are not in a straight line but are curved. These natural drainage areas should be set aside in the land plan for potential drainage conveyance. If there should be several drainage areas within the site, the land plan should evaluate each separate drainage area for cost-effective design. The costs associated with altering the natural drainage area on site would increase per lot costs. The alterations changing the natural flow of the site would not be well received by the regulatory reviewer.

Environment

The base map (otherwise the boundary map), if prepared, must show the wetland areas, wetland buffers, and 100-year flood plain areas. Land set aside for environmental protection reduces the flexibility of the land plan and reduces the number of potential lots within the subdivision. The net buildable area will establish the lot yield and lot costs for land development activities.

Soils

Investigate the existing soil characteristics of the site. Most sites have two or more soil types. The type of soil could affect the way the project is developed. The land plan should recognize the soil types and use this information to the benefit of the project. As an example, the soil types with excellent infiltration capabilities should be used for septic systems and/or drainage basin designs. High groundwater and unsuitable soil, rock, clay, or soil excavated for a profit should be fully addressed during the land plan and engineering design phases.

Vegetation

Other site characteristics to be indicated on the base plan are existing trees, which should be preserved because of the species, size, or characteristic. The trees

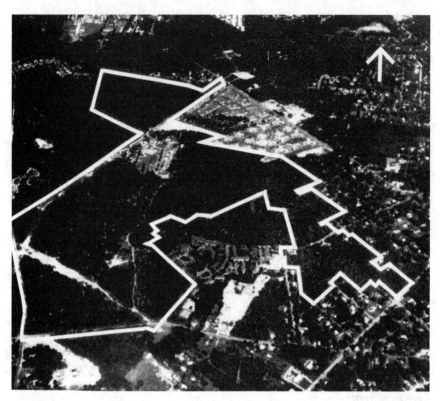

Photo 7-2. Aerial Views. An aerial view is a valuable tool for land planning and for understanding the relationship of the site to adjacent land uses and public improvements.

should be shown on the base map, and the land plan should attempt to use this site characteristic to the benefit of the project. The replacement of mature landscaping with like material within a project would be cost prohibitive. However, the market potential for saving significant trees onsite or transplanting the trees onsite with the use of a tree spade can be substantial and certainly outweighs the cost of replanting.

Utilities

The base map should also show the locations of all utilities that serve the project site. Sewer lines should be shown, including any manhole connections, inverts, and rim elevations. Water lines should be indicated on the plan, showing the size, type, and class of pipe. Locate all fire hydrants and valves. Gas mains, overhead electric lines, telephone poles, and drainage culverts under existing roadways or street inlets and connecting storm drains must be indicated on the plan. All of this information is compiled on one boundary and topography survey base map. All

Photo 7-3. Opportunities and Constraints Plan. This illustrative plan shows the site analysis and base map information for a site. This plan is used for land planning and public presentation purposes.

of the elements of the site need to be considered during the conceptual land planning phase.

HOUSING PRODUCT

The land planner should meet with the builder/developer to determine the housing product planned for the site. To successfully market single-family subdivisions, the project should be different from the competition. The site analysis and conceptual land planning phases identify the site characteristics and constraints

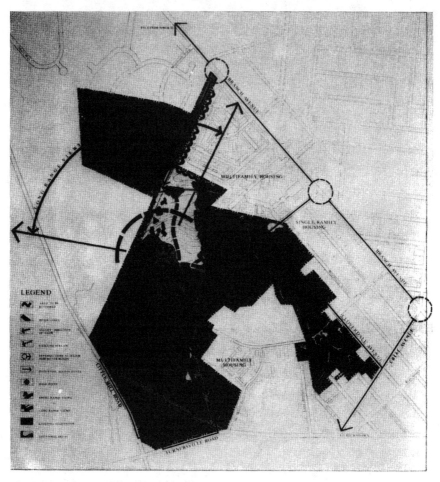

Photo 7-4. Visual Analysis Plan. This plan is an illustration of the site's benefits. The benefits become important marketing tools and should be incorporated in the land planning of the site.

that must be incorporated into the design. If used properly, the site attributes will be maximized to their greatest market potential. The housing product presented in the project will complement the site characteristics. This will enhance the marketability of the homes and increase absorption.

Select the housing type that complements the terrain and the site characteristics to minimize land development costs. If the land and land development costs are lower than those of the competition, the homes can be offered at a greater value. Homebuyers understand value and competition comparison. If the project has value, they will purchase the product regardless of whether the value is real or perceived. If the difference in land and land development costs is taken as profit, there will not be any significant difference between competitive projects. Share the profit with value and site uniqueness to succeed.

During the planning phase, consider various foundation types and select the appropriate type for the marketplace and the site.

- *Basements.* Basements are ideal for generating fill and adding to the value of the home. Basements have an excellent perceived value, and if the site topography has dramatic changes, basement homes can provide flexibility in grading and clearing work.
- *Side-to-side and front-to-back splits.* This housing type uses the ground to establish greater market appeal, and the cost savings can be used for added values.
- *Crawl spaces and basements.* These features allow minimal clearing of lots for housing construction. The minimum distance from the finished floor elevation to the finished grade should be no less than 1.7 ft.
- *Slab construction.* These foundations are excellent for flat areas. Pads for slab foundations have to be created during earthwork operations. The minimum distance from the finished floor elevation to the finished grade should be no less than 0.7 ft.

Consider other types of housing styles that can be used in areas where the terrain varies in elevation, such as garages under the home, split levels, walkout basements, etc. The housing design and land plan are complementing elements that, if approached with practical market and design sense, will increase sales and provide customer referrals.

The capability to develop and build the project in phases reduces cashflow requirements and regulatory commitments. Proper project phasing is another key element of success. The goal is to provide as many lots as possible for the least amount of infrastructure expense. This approach is advantageous for cashflow purposes and customer lot selection. The design of the project phases should include a mix of quality lots. Always keep the best located lots for the latter phases. These lots will always sell. Establishing premiums on quality lots will help in selling the less attractive lot locations first. Builder/developers do not want to be faced with disposal of the undesirable lots at the end of the project. The housing presentation for the initial phase will establish the tone for the remaining phases of the project.

COVENANTS, CONDITIONS, AND RESTRICTIONS

If the business plan includes selling lots to outside builders or to individual lot purchasers, architectural covenants and restrictions should be developed and included in the marketing plan for the lots. The basic elements of covenants, conditions, and restrictions (CCRs) follow.

Description of Permitted Uses

This statement is based on the zoning regulations imposed by local government. It can be expanded to include specific accessory uses and buildings such as sheds, detached garages, or other types of buildings that could be constructed on the lot. The description of the permitted uses would control the aesthetic appearance of each lot. Controlling the street scene will maintain property values and support the sales effort for lots or homes in the subdivision.

Type of Building

If the housing product is a ranch or a two-story colonial style and the preference is to have that type of product built in the subdivision, the building restrictions should be included in the CCRs. The CCRs can be more restrictive than local zoning and planning ordinances. Typically, the type of building is judged on the style and size of the house; for example, the only houses permitted will be at least 2,000 ft^2, two-story colonial, contemporary with a two-car garage. These types of building restrictions can be included in the CCRs to govern the future build out of the project site.

Height Restrictions

Height restrictions can be imposed in the CCRs by limiting the style of the house to one, two, or three stories. This restriction will also set the project apart from the competition. The height restrictions must meet the bulk requirements of the zone.

Setbacks

The setbacks from the street, side yards, or rear yard generally complement local zoning bulk requirements but can be more restrictive for accessory buildings and garages.

Architectural Restrictions

Architectural restrictions can be expanded to include exterior colors of housing products, such as shingles, siding, garage doors, front doors, shutters, etc. Preapproved types of windows, front doors, and garage door materials can be included in the restrictions. For instance, using steel or aluminum garage doors, paneled or flat, with or without sunbursts would be included in the CCRs.

Architectural restrictions are imposed to maintain the aesthetic appearance of the street scene. The architectural restrictions could include a look-alike provision, which prohibits similar exterior housing elevations from being constructed adjacent to or across the street from each other. Particular attention should be made to the roofline, window locations, colors, and door styles. Facade materials such as vinyl, wood, brick, stone, etc., and the quality of the material could be dictated in the CCRs to control the house types in a subdivision.

When the information in the CCRs is vague, its interpretation is open to each individual owner or builder. When restrictions are imposed and the effort is extended to manage the CCR provisions, it is incumbent on the author of the

Photo 7-5. Covenants, Conditions, and Restrictions. Covenants, conditions, and restrictions provide a legal means to control the use and appearance of the homes constructed in a subdivision.

CCR to develop a guideline that is very specific in terms of criteria and standards to be followed by each lot owner. A sample outline of a CCR document, which can be used for single-family subdivisions, is provided in Figure 7-3.

Another aspect of implementing CCRs is the single requirement that all proposed house plans be approved by the developer. The developer reviews the house plans, the material specifications, and the construction specifications before any building permits are issued. This benchmark is inserted into CCRs to ensure that all homes meet the standards for the project. Also, in the CCRs, a variance or an appeal process must be provided to give each individual lot owner an opportunity to meet or strive to meet the intent of the CCRs.

CCRs are imposed to maintain property values and control individual taste. The results of implementing this type of control will be consistency in housing styles. CCRs review the individual design approaches and compare them to the subdivision as a whole for a homogeneous but individualistic subdivision appearance.

AN EXAMPLE FOR A SINGLE-FAMILY HOME SUBDIVISION

In order to preserve the character and integrity of a residential community and to protect the value of the homes therein, the declarant hereby declares that the homes and property shall be subject to all CCRs of record and to the following restrictions, all of which shall be perpetual in duration and run with the land:

1. No noxious or offensive activities shall be carried on, in, or upon the property or in any home, nor shall anything be done there either willfully or negligently, which may be or may become an annoyance or nuisance to the other residents in the subdivision.

2. Each home constructed on each lot must consist of no less than 1,750 ft^2 of living space. The design of said home shall be of a style that is compatible with all other homes within the entire tract and the property. No home shall be constructed, no outbuilding or accessory building shall be constructed, and no addition or alteration shall be made to any existing building without the prior written approval of the declarant. All plans and renderings shall be submitted to the declarant for approval at least 30 days before any applications are filed for a building permit.

3. The declarant shall have a reasonable period of time, but less than 30 days, to review the same. If the plans and renderings are, in the sole discretion of the declarant, contrary to the provisions of this paragraph, the homeowner shall be prohibited from submitting the same for a building permit. The homeowner shall revise or modify the plans and renderings to comply with the design and size requirements of this paragraph and resubmit the same to the declarant. Thereupon the review period shall begin again.

ARCHITECTURAL REVIEW

1. No building, fence, wall, structure, or any improvement shall be erected on the owner's lot, nor shall any exterior change to the color scheme or alteration be made until the plans and specifications showing the nature, height, materials, colors, and location of change have been submitted in writing to the architectural control committee. Such committee shall be established as provided in the Homeowners Association (HOA) bylaws. In the event said committee fails to approve or reject, with or without condition, the application within 30 days after submission, approval will be deemed to have been granted without conditions. The architectural review committee shall adopt design criteria and standards for architectural control.

2. No owner shall erect or maintain an antenna on any lot.

3. The owner of each dwelling unit or lot shall maintain the building or lot in good order and repair and be consistent with all those CCRs, rules, and regulations as may apply to the building or lots. In the event that a dwelling unit, lot, or parcel shall not be so maintained, the HOA shall have the right to enter the building or lot to maintain the same, after giving the owner at least 20 days' written notice, to cure any maintenance problems. The HOA shall have the right to assess the owner for the cost of such maintenance. The

architectural review committee shall establish rules and regulations governing the exterior maintenance of any building or lots.

4. No owner shall carry on any practice, or permit any practice to be carried on, that unreasonably interferes with the quiet enjoyment by any other owner.

5. Each owner of a dwelling unit shall maintain fire and extended coverage insurance.

6. No owner shall leave any nonoperating vehicle or unlicensed vehicle on the lot so as to be visible from any neighboring lot.

7. No owner shall be permitted to lease his or her dwelling unit unless the lease has been submitted in writing to the architectural review committee for approval. All leases shall provide that the lease shall be subject, in all respects, to the provisions of the bylaws, the declaration of CCRs, and rules and regulations of the HOA.

8. No above-ground swimming pools may be erected on any lot.

9. No trailers, vans, storage tanks, temporary structures, or accessory buildings shall be erected on any lot without the approval of the architectural review committee.

10. No recreational vehicles, trucks, or boats shall be parked or stored on any lot.

11. No unsightly weeds, underbrush, or other unsightly vegetation shall be permitted to grow or remain on any lot.

Figure 7-4 outlines a comprehensive approach that developers can follow to transition a residential infrastructure to an HOA. This approach is applicable for planned unit developments, small clustered subdivisions, and traditional subdivisions with common elements, such as stormwater management facilities. At the completion of a residential housing project, the improvements must be transferred by ownership to another entity. Concentrate on turning over improvements as soon as it is practical. Use the outline to ensure that all issues are adequately addressed. Thus, the entity required to accept the improvements cannot find any reason not to accept the facilities, and the reputation of the developer is further enhanced.

CONCEPTUAL COST ESTIMATE

On the completion of the land plan, prepare a conceptual land development cost estimate. Preparing an estimate without design information is appropriate to ascertain the viability of the project design. This approach also provides the opportunity to identify all of the land development costs before proceeding with the project. Estimating the finished lot cost based on the conceptual land plan provides an excellent way to assess the lot yield, land development costs, and sales prices.

Figure 7-5 is a cost-estimate form that can be used in developing the conceptual cost estimate for the project. The comments category should be used to indicate how those costs were calculated. This form also provides the means to review the project costs as the preliminary and final designs are prepared. In Figure 7-5, in the absence of specific design detail, use the rule of thumb included after each line item. The estimate prepared should be used as a guideline and represent the conservative approach to land development. Include all of the costs in the cashflow analysis or project pro forma. Figure 7-6 is a typical houseline budget form to be used for conceptual cost analysis purposes. Calculate the land development costs per unit. If the goals can be achieved by adding these costs to the other project costs and the housing sales price, the proposed land plan works. Figure 7-7 is a basic project pro forma that highlights the major cost items for a housing project.

This cost foundation also provides the financial framework to determine what the project can afford and what can be compromised during the regulatory process. Refinements of the land plan will improve the marketability of the project. If the costs are substantially higher than those budgeted in the project pro forma, the land plan should be redesigned to reduce infrastructure costs, increase the number of lots, or a combination of both. Consideration should be given to the fact that perhaps the project's raw land price may be too high to sell houses and make a profit. It is conceivable that the value of the property is overinflated, which is generally the case for people who have owned their property for a long period of time. Many landowners arbitrarily establish an unrealistic value for their property, which may eliminate the profit for the project. If the conceptual cost estimate and pro forma price the project out of the market, do not force the issue. Stay with the housing goals and keep searching for the best-suited property for the marketplace. The conceptual land plan and cost estimate are excellent tools for negotiating the land purchase. If the cashflow analysis for the project shows that the property is properly designed for its highest and best use, proceed with serious negotiations for the purchase of the land.

CHAPTER 8

Residential Subdivision Design

Once the conceptual land plan has been approved, the infrastructure of the subdivision will be designed by an engineering firm. There are many regulatory requirements and design criteria governing subdivision design work. However, there are many construction approaches that should be reviewed in detail to enhance the subdivision's appearance and function while substantially reducing the land development cost of the project. The initial discussions with the engineering firm should focus on design items for cost savings that could be incorporated into the preliminary design documents.

The alternative approaches conveyed in this chapter are valid ways to meet the intent of the regulatory engineering design standards. If acceptable to the local government engineer, the project can achieve success both financially and aesthetically. If the locale does not accept these ideas, the community may have more stringent subdivision standards and, most likely, higher housing prices. Designing residential subdivisions with standards based on conservative engineering and planning criteria adds substantial development costs with debatable benefits.

DESIGN APPROACHES

The following design approaches should be used as a guide in discussions with the engineering design team before preparation of the preliminary construction documents.

Clearing

Limit the amount of clearing necessary to construct the subdivision. If selling lots to builders or individual buyers, the design plans should show the clearing of the right-of-way and a 10-ft strip of land beyond the right-of-way line for the construction of the roads. If building on the lots, the plans should show minimum clearing of the lot. Show no less than 10 ft around a dwelling unit and 20 to 30 ft in the rear yard.

If allowed by law or permitted, it is cost effective to burn the material cleared onsite. If burning is not permitted, stumps and debris will have to be trucked to a landfill. It may be permitted to bury the stumps in an open-space berm that would not be sold by the homeowners. The following clearing operation alternatives would result in a cost savings to the project:

Trees can be chipped onsite. The pile of wood chips should be stockpiled in a cleared area out of the way of subsequent infrastructure construction. The chips can be used for ground cover within the tree-save areas. Also, many homeowners take the chips for use in their own yards. If the chips are not used as noted, the contractor can sell the wood chips and further reduce the contractual cost for clearing. Stumping the cleared area can result in substantial amounts of debris that would be removed from the job site. Renting a stump grinding machine provides the contractor a cost-effective method for disposal of stumps. This machine grinds the stumps into mulch. This mulch can be mixed with topsoil and used onsite for open-space top dressing. Grinding stumps and chipping trees onsite would reduce or eliminate the cost of trucking the material offsite to a landfill.

Staking out specimen trees within the site by a surveyor is the best approach for a residential subdivision. The cost of clearing may increase on a per-lot or per-acre basis because it is considered selective clearing. However, saving trees only enhances the subdivision's appearance and adds to the value of the lots. The benefit of selective clearing is greater than the cost associated with this type of operation. This is true even if the trees saved are not specimen trees. Narrower roads will reduce the right-of-way requirements and the amount of clearing. Most residential subdivisions have a 50-ft right-of-way that should be reduced to 2 ft beyond the curbline. This approach would save trees, reduce costs, and add land to tax-paying property owners. If the government will not accept narrow pavement widths or right-of-way widths, design the subdivision with private roads, which would not have a public right-of-way. The lot lines become the property line of the roadway located at the edge of pavement. A private road system would have to be owned and maintained by an HOA. Private roads would be beneficial to the project. However, will this approach be judged as a negative because each home would be governed by an HOA? The ownership and maintenance of private roadways by owners of single-family detached homes may be viewed as an added burden and a negative marketing approach. The benefit of saving trees and marketing an environmentally sensitive subdivision should outweigh the perceived burden. In some cases, contractors will provide a much lower unit price if they can maximize the use of their equipment. Thus, in terms of phasing a project, look at the phased construction to maximize the clearing work for each phase so the equipment is used to its maximum capability.

Earthwork

The engineer should design the project to balance the cuts and fills on the site. Always minimize the cost to import material. The moving of material more than

Photo 8-1. Earthwork. Balancing the cuts and fills of a project is an art in design. Properly managing earthwork operation is critical because of its complexity. The need to import fill will be minimized when the engineering design uses the topography of the site to benefit the design.

once within a project site can be minimized if large cuts and fills are avoided. Large cuts and fills generally require many staging areas for the excavated material before its use. The clearing of land for stockpiling of excavated material may require clearing beyond the current phase of lots. To maximize the cashflow at the start of a project, carefully review the clearing and earthwork operational requirements for the initial phase. Locate any staging areas in the last phase of the project, if possible.

The engineer should design the vertical and horizontal subdivision road alignments to complement the topography of the land. Road alignments should follow the terrain by being parallel or perpendicular to the contour lines as much as possible. It is preferable to design the roadways in a cut condition so that the lots automatically become higher than the roadway. This approach would facilitate proper lot drainage, allowing the maximum number of trees to be saved.

The lot topsoil after clearing and grubbing operations should be stockpiled in a location that can always be used and not interfere with subsequent infrastructure development and/or housing operations. Stockpiling locations for topsoil or excess material should be reviewed with the engineer at the very start of the design process.

To control earthwork costs, balance the cuts and fills or minimize the distance for hauling the material from one location onsite to another. It is preferable to use pans versus trucks and loaders simply because of the efficiency and the cost difference between the two methods.

Rock areas, or areas of any unsuitable material identified during the site analysis work, are important to avoid in the land planning of the site. The design engineer will use the soils information as a guide during the initial design phase.

The housing foundation design will also affect earthwork quantities and operations. Consideration should be given to the overall architectural design approach to the subdivision. The design engineer needs to know the type of housing product and the foundation design. The engineer can grade the lots according to the architectural approach, and the cost of earthwork operations can further be identified. If individual lots are sold as "buildable" lots, and housing pads are constructed, decide on a clear definition of "buildable" for the specific housing type.

Sanitary Sewer Design

Sanitary sewer design is governed by standard regulatory approaches handed down from year to year and from state to state. However, the following ideas can at least be discussed with design engineers to provide an appropriate system at the least cost.

Design for the minimum-diameter pipe size allowed by regulation. Use 6-inch diameter lines with clean outs wherever possible, instead of the standard 8-inch line with manholes.

The alignment of the sewer line often is located along the centerline of the public roadway. Maximize the distance between manholes. Design a minimum of 400 ft between manholes, and use easements on the lots if necessary. Locating sewer lines on lots located on the inside of horizontal curves may encumber the property. Easements within the front setback would be an acceptable and cost-effective approach.

Use pipe slopes that minimize the trench and manhole depths. If possible, keep all sewer lines within 8 ft of the surface. An 8-ft trench depth can be excavated with less expensive equipment. More shallow pipe installations are easier and quicker. The cost and schedule of the project will be properly managed with this design approach. The design engineer should review the soils information to determine rock croppings or unsuitable soil locations. This information is useful for designing sewer lines or other utilities at the least cost.

In a cul-de-sac, extend the sewer line far enough to allow access to the last lots by maximizing the length of the lateral line providing service to those lots. This would eliminate the need to extend the main trunk line closer to the lot.

The type of pipe material will also affect the cost of the sewer line. The use of polyvinyl chloride (PVC) pipe for sanitary sewers is recognized in many municipalities. This pipe costs substantially less than any other type of pipe material used for sanitary sewer lines.

Connecting the project to an offsite sewer line with a gravity line or with a pump station/force main system must be analyzed from a first cost and maintenance basis. An alternative system to the gravity sewer is the pressure sewer system. This sewer system uses grinder, or effluent, pumps at each individual house and is approved for use by many governmental agencies. Each home uses a 2-inch force main connecting to a 4-inch collector force main in a street. Ultimately, the lines are connected to an outlet manhole or gravity sewer line. The pressure sewer system is more cost effective than a gravity sewer line design but may meet consumer objections.

Water Distribution

There are three ways to reduce the cost of water distribution systems:

- Minimize the length of lateral lines to each lot.
- Investigate the possibility of using pipe sizes of 4 and 6 inches.
- Use PVC material instead of ductile iron pipe (DIP) material.

Joint trenching with sewer or other utility lines would also reduce costs. Locate fire hydrants in accordance with local fire department regulations. On the plans, the design engineer should scale a 250-ft radius circle around each fire hydrant. To ensure full fire service coverage in the subdivision, every home should be located within the circular area surrounding the fire hydrants. In locating fire hydrants, a linear approach using 500 ft between fire hydrants can also be used in design.

For single-family houses, use one connection to a property line and then use a Y-connection to the individual homes. This design approach should be coordinated with the other utility line designs. This will ensure that conflicts with street lights, transformer locations, or cable television pedestals are minimized. Most utility companies design their structural facilities on common property lines. By minimizing the pipe size, although the cost difference between pipe sizes is not significant, there will be a cost savings. The design engineer should evaluate when pipe sizes can be reduced once the service area is further reduced.

There is a dramatic cost difference between PVC pipe and the more expensive DIP material. If the local jurisdiction does not permit the use of PVC pipe, provide documentation and information for their review. Longevity, maintenance capabilities, and the ease of installation are positive attributes of PVC pipe. Take the opportunity to seek approvals for alternative pipe materials for residential subdivisions.

Drainage

To minimize the infrastructure cost for drainage facilities, the designer should use the site topography to benefit the stormwater management facility and drainage system design for the project. Rather than making substantial changes to the land profile, the natural contour of the land should be used for drainage swales and retention of stormwater before it flows from the project site. The land planner needs to use the natural landform regardless of its location. However, if the location substantially affects the lot yield, alternative land plans are required. In most cases, the natural flow of the property can be used and stormwater management facilities need not be a detriment to the project.

Stormwater management facilities can be used as a positive marketing tool. Detention ponds are valid open-space areas, and retention ponds can be designed with permanent water surfaces. Premiums can be charged for lots bordering these facilities. Minimizing storm drainage costs is basic to a well-visualized land plan that uses the topography to its maximum potential. This approach would result in locating several stormwater management facilities in subareas and would minimize the number of inlets, pipe lengths, and stormwater management facilities.

Minimize pipe lengths by taking road drainage from inlets directly to natural drainage swales or stormwater management facilities. This will eliminate multiple connections to inlets, which will also result in an increase in downstream pipe diameters. Larger pipe sizes will increase the cost of construction.

Maximize the length of gutter flow and the spread of water in the street to minimize the number of drainage inlets. Many municipalities are requiring the design of subdivision drainage systems to be based on a 25-year storm. This conservative design approach undermines the cost efficiency of residential subdivisions without a true benefit. A 10-year storm design approach is adequate for housing developments.

Designing a system using minimum pipe sizes will minimize material cost and trenching costs. Pipe material such as corrugated metal pipe could be an alternative, but this pipe is larger in size than reinforced concrete pipe (RCP) serving the same watershed. The cost in trenching and installation, combined with the problems associated with the availability of corrugated metal pipe, equals the cost of using RCP. Most municipal governments that accept the responsibility and the maintenance of drainage systems in subdivisions prefer to use RCP. Obtaining local government approval for alternative pipe material will demand the additional use of corporate resources, delay the approval process, and result in only marginal cost savings.

The location of stormwater management facilities and detention or retention ponds should benefit the maximum number of housing units in the subdivision. The detention of stormwater involves controlling the runoff for a period of time and then gradually releasing the water from the site to adjacent properties at a rate no greater than the runoff generated from an undisturbed site. Retention basins retain the stormwater in a pond and use either evaporation or infiltration to lower the water level. This permits runoff of future storm events to enter the pond and be treated before release. Stormwater management ponds should be designed as a subdivision feature. Ponds can be designed as entry features or as open-space features within a subdivision.

In locations with high groundwater, a permanent water surface in a stormwater management facility can be supplemented by a shallow well pumping water into the pond. If high groundwater exists and overexcavation is permitted, the pond area can be a source of fill material by the overexcavation.

In locations where it is not cost effective to pipe stormwater to a drainage facility, design a recharge system that uses perforated corrugated aluminum pipe and stone trenches to store the water and release the water by infiltration. Although the system is expensive, the cost of the system may be less than that of a complex closed drainage system with multiple inlets, manholes, and larger pipe sizes or may be less than losing a lot for a stormwater basin.

Piping rain leaders from the housing units into dry wells is another way to effectively reduce the amount of stormwater conveyed to a closed drainage system in the street. This approach is cost effective if the local municipality agrees that a reduced impervious-surface percentage can be used in the drainage calculations. This approach would effectively reduce street pipe sizes, and yards will be protected from erosion problems. Installing rain leaders to dry wells when the house is under construction would eliminate yard erosion and eliminate extra expense for grading the lot. Drainage facilities are the most regulated design elements of a housing project. It is important for the design engineer to emphasize and devote time to this issue in order to reduce, minimize, and eliminate costly drainage facilities in a subdivision. The cost savings can be significant. However, multiple reviewing agencies will have a direct effect on accomplishing and implementing some of these ideas. It may take a devoted regulatory lobbying effort to change the subdivision regulations to include new proven design ideas.

Roadway

The roadway design can minimize earthwork by using the existing topography. If the roadway is in a cut, the housing units can be left above the roadway. This approach would ensure proper lot drainage and street drainage can be accommodated more cost effectively. If there is onsite material that can be used for road base, and the material is permitted by the local municipality, project costs will be reduced.

A reduction in pavement widths can result in perhaps the greatest cost savings. Without question, most municipality residential street width requirements are conservative and overly restrictive for the intended use. As a rule of thumb, the cost for a 30-ft roadway width and a 50-ft right-of-way width can range from $150 to $200 per linear foot of improvement. Any reduction in pavement widths will significantly reduce the per linear footage cost. Most municipalities have standard asphalt pavement requirements. Consideration should be given to alternative pavement mixes that can provide reduced costs, be environmentally sensitive, and be more readily available. The type of curbing required for residential subdivision design is based on local use. Various design alternatives could include asphalt rolled curb, standard L-block type barrier curb, or concrete mountable curb. In the Northeast, Belgian block curb is used in most subdivisions. The initial cost for Belgian block curb is higher, but the marketing potential in a quality subdivision is tremendous. Also, the ease and cost to replace damaged Belgian block curb are substantially less than for other curb types.

The debate of public versus private roadways has been voiced in numerous communities in every state. All opportunities to design single-family detached housing subdivisions with private streets should be reviewed during the project feasibility phase. This alternative infrastructure approach has wide market appeal. The upfront or initial cost of private roads is less than for public roads. However, an HOA must be created to maintain and operate the roads. There will be a monthly HOA fee for the private facilities. There are, however, adverse marketing reasons to private roads because of the creation of an HOA. In single-family detached neighborhoods, the lot owners would prefer a level of independence and not have restrictions imposed and enforced by an HOA. The infrastructure constructed needs to be of high quality to ensure the level of maintenance is reduced.

DESIGN QUALITY

Quality infrastructure also reduces the cash reserves required of an association for replacement of infrastructure elements. Negotiating with reputable land devel-

Photo 8-2. Design and Construction. Creative design approaches are required to reduce costs, minimize fill problems, and achieve quality living environments.

opment contractors that are known and have been in business for more than several years is another key objective to reduce costs. If any portion of the infrastructure fails, there is a need to seek corrective measures from the contractor. The contractor should provide a 2-year warranty for their work.

These land development design elements are guidelines to be used in creating a pattern of development that would add to the overall market appeal of the project, while reducing costs. These ideas can only be implemented if the regulatory agencies are in agreement with the design approach.

Once the design review is complete, the project will have final construction documents available for submission to regulatory agencies. These plans include sufficient detail necessary for bid estimates to be obtained from land development contractors. The plans must be complete and must comply with the regulations of the local municipal government. If not, the plans can be deemed incomplete and returned with an extensive review list prepared by the reviewing engineer. Both conclusions would delay the project in the regulatory process. Any negotiations or discussions on design alternatives may or may not be resolved in the short term. Thus, review the design plans to ensure they are prepared to the best of the design group's ability. The project design may have a better chance of an approval on the first submission if the regulatory agency's design preferences are used in the project.

ENGINEERING REVIEW

Figure 8-1 is prepared for use by the builder/developer in reviewing engineering plans before regulatory submission. This checklist is not intended to double-check the design characteristics of a plan. That is the responsibility of the registered engineer. This checklist is a guideline to be used to verify the information required by regulatory engineers is indeed in the plans. A concise review of the plans using this checklist ensures that the project's construction documents are as complete as possible before submission. The development goals should be reflected in the engineering plans and reports. As an example, basements and crawl spaces have greater market appeal than slab construction. The engineering plans should reflect the proper grading around the houses. The finished floor elevation relationship to the exterior grade must be consistent with a model building code.

COST ESTIMATE

After reviewing the engineering plans, an in-house land development cost budget should be prepared for the project. Figure 8-2 is a comprehensive land development budget form to be used at the preliminary engineering design phase. This budget document is intended to highlight key elements of the land development process. The preliminary estimate should be based on current unit prices and current material and labor prices. The comment portion of the form provides an opportunity to explain the cost approach taken for each line item. This estimate will be used in the contractual negotiations with land development contractors in order to verify their costs. This preliminary estimate is used in the project pro forma to verify the sales price for the lots or homes in the project. A comparison of the preliminary cost versus the conceptual cost will provide significant insight on the ability to meet the market demands. The preliminary budget for land development will also identify items that could result in a cost savings. Areas that differ drastically from the conceptual land development budget will be highlighted. This review and costing procedure allows the owner a chance to analyze the overall approach to the project and make changes for financial and market reasons. The opportunity to change the plans for financial or market reasons must be taken before the plans are submitted to the regulatory agency. Governmental inspection and escrow fees continue to escalate during the review process of any subdivision plan. Thus, it is prudent business sense to carefully review the engineering plans before submission. Make sure the plans are consistent with company goals, and identify any cost issues that may be drastically different than originally anticipated.

CHAPTER 9

Residential Land Development Standards

Over the past several years, participants of the American Society of Civil Engineers (ASCE) seminar "Residential Land Development Practices" have provided data on the residential street standards used in their locales. The participants have been design engineers, regulatory engineers, and development engineers. Data have been compiled from all sectors of the country. The intent of this chapter on residential land development standards is to analyze the variety of standards and use this information in the development of a set of criteria that could be used as a guide by the practicing engineer. It is clear that the criteria engineers must use to design residential streets are inconsistent, and some of the standards used have no engineering basis. Many standards are developed locally and modified politically to establish local control over the residential land development industry. Some states require that regional residential street standards be used by all municipalities within that region. Engineers must evaluate their current standards against the following criteria to ensure the standards adopted are efficient and cost effective and protect the health safety and welfare of the citizens.

There are certain health, safety, and welfare issues that need to be considered in developing appropriate engineering standards for residential subdivisions. This approach needs to be counterbalanced with the cost benefit to the initial user and to the ultimately responsible party—the local government. The cost of housing will continue to increase as standards become all too conservative, and the cost to develop residential subdivisions will continue to rise.

The following standards should be used as a guide in the review of current standards or in the development of standards for engineering design of residential subdivisions.

RESIDENTIAL STREETS

It is clear that the street standards imposed by most municipalities are still vehicular oriented rather than pedestrian oriented. The historical view of the development of residential streets has resulted in a "bigger is better" philosophy. This is a dramatic demarcation from the way our cities were originally planned and developed. This is primarily a result of the use of cars and the standard and style of living to which we have become accustomed. It would seem that the engineering criteria used to design streets should be somewhat similar across the country with obvious localized changes.

Through the compilation of these design data and discussions with engineers across the country, a consensus established the following residential street design standards as the basis on which to prepare a land development design ordinance.

RIGHT-OF-WAY

Most municipalities use a 50-ft right-of-way for local residential streets. The right-of-way will change as the number of lots or average daily traffic (ADT) changes for a road segment. However, there were several municipalities that required a 60-ft right-of-way for a local subdivision street. From a design point of view, the additional right-of-way does not significantly protect the public welfare and basically results in the removal of additional land from the tax roles.

PAVEMENT WIDTH

The participants of the survey indicated more than 20 different residential street widths. The most common standard used for pavement width of a local residential street was 28 ft, which can be substantiated by having an 8-ft parking lane on one side of the street and having two 10-ft travel lanes. It would be important for the municipality to establish a hierarchy of roadway widths to accommodate vehicular movement. This approach would use the 28-ft width as a standard for a residential subdivision. The width would increase AND decrease as the number of units using the road varies. The establishment of the hierarchy of road widths would be based on ADT values for residential uses. This ADT value should be established at the local level, but it would not be unreasonable to have a threshold of 1,500 ADT for the 28-ft pavement width.

CUL-DE-SACS

The most common dimensions for a cul-de-sac are a 50-ft radius right-of-way and a 40-ft pavement radius. The length of a cul-de-sac varies considerably, but the consensus was between 600 and 1,200 ft. The reason for the variance is because the length of a cul-de-sac is set by local preferences. There are many regulations that impose a maximum number of units to be served by a cul-de-sac. The most common number of units permitted on a cul-de-sac is 25 homes.

CURBS AND SIDEWALKS

Most new residential streets are required to have curbs, which provide for pavement protection and drainage conveyance. Most new residential streets also have 4-ft sidewalks on both sides of the street.

VERTICAL AND HORIZONTAL CURVES

A local ordinance should provide the minimum and maximum grades for vertical curves. Most jurisdictions require 0.5% minimum and 10% maximum grades for residential streets. Certainly, there are many states in which the 0.5% grade may be too steep and the 10% grade may not be steep enough. Depending on the topography of the area, these standards should be modified to ensure that the engineering design can easily accommodate the existing lay of the land, can minimize earthwork, and can potentially save more existing vegetation onsite. The maximum grade within 100 ft of a street intersection should be 6%.

The minimum horizontal curve for residential streets should be 100 ft. This criterion would provide engineers with design flexibility and would not jeopardize the health, safety, and welfare of the users. The horizontal alignment dictates the speed of the drivers in residential applications. The goal of residential street design is to put more emphasis on the pedestrians and homeowners and less on vehicle movement. Residential street design should not be based on a design speed; it should be designed to limit vehicle speed within a housing subdivision. The most common pavement cross-slope is 2%.

The angle of an intersection does not have to be set at 90 degrees. Most ordinances allow an intersection of not less than 75 degrees. Intersection design for residential uses should permit this flexibility, but designing an intersection at less than 90 degrees should be the exception and not the rule.

On major highways and collector roadways, tangents between reverse curves are important in the design of the horizontal alignment. However, in the design of residential streets, where slower speeds are encouraged, a tangent between reverse curves becomes less important.

WATER AND SEWER LINES

It is common practice throughout the United States to have a minimum pipe size of 6 and 8 inches for both water and sewer lines. In most jurisdictions, PVC pipe is the preferred pipe material for both water and sewer lines. The distance between fire hydrants is 500 ft. The distance between sewer manholes is 400 ft.

DRAINAGE

This element of residential infrastructure design remains very site specific because of the climate differences across the country. Also, there seem to be many overlapping reviewing agencies that at times have different criteria for designing drainage facilities for residential subdivisions. Most ordinances require stormwater management facilities to be addressed on a project basis. This adds to the overall cost of the community drainage facilities for the maintenance of isolated systems. Most communities have not instituted regional stormwater management planning. Jurisdictions that have planned to control stormwater on a watershed basis have found benefits in centralizing the facilities for maintenance purposes.

The intent of stormwater management is to control the runoff generated by a subdivision after development and to discharge it at a rate less than or equal to the rate generated before development. Roadway drainage facilities are designed using a 10-year storm event. The maximum spacing between inlets is 400 ft. There are jurisdictions that use the spread of water in the travel lane to determine the inlet spacing. The minimum size for a storm drain pipe in most jurisdictions is 15 inches. There are communities that permit a 12-inch pipe, and some require a minimum pipe size of 18 inches.

CHAPTER 10

Project Approval Strategy

All housing projects have an impact on the local community in which the subdivision is located. In most cases, the impact on the immediate area or community is positive. During the regulatory process, the builder/developer should initiate a proactive public relations program to involve, inform, and educate the residents within the community about the proposed benefits of the project.

Being sensitive to existing neighborhood concerns will help minimize local opposition to the project. The builder/developer has to investigate and seek to understand the needs and priorities of the community. By doing this, the project can be presented as a "good neighbor" during public hearings, during the regulatory permitting process, during the sale of homes, and after homes have closed in the subdivision.

There must be a commitment to communication. Communication will enhance the company's ability to gain support from the community. This commitment to communication will convey the positive aspects of the project to the general public. A general positive community awareness and neighborhood support of the project will be beneficial in obtaining government approvals. It will also allow the homes to be introduced into the marketplace in a timely manner. At the initial sales release, the commitment to communication will have created a positive environment for homebuyers to purchase.

APPROVAL STRATEGY

The following issues are important for a builder/developer to follow in creating a project approval strategy. Many of these issues are taken for granted, but their outcome ultimately determines the success or failure of the project presentation before planning boards.

Experts

Design professionals and consultants are often very good at the design and technical aspects of a housing project, but seldom do they have the ability to convey that message before a public audience. In getting to know the consultants, it is advisable to understand their ability to take technical information, dissect it, and present it in lay terms. The general audience and planning board members must not be talked down to in technical jargon.

If the project design information is technically acceptable but cannot be adequately conveyed, the planning board members may impose unacceptable conditions or pass a negative vote on the project. Thus, it is incumbent on the builder/developer to observe the consultant's presentation of a project during a public forum. At the very least meet with them for an extended time to understand how they express their thoughts and how they may convey technical information to audiences.

Political Problems

Housing projects require strategies to be created for gaining governmental acceptance of the subdivision project. Local community political issues need to be examined if it is anticipated that local government wishes to have its problems resolved by new developments. By understanding its problems, solutions can be incorporated into the design, and answers to the problems can be conveyed during the public hearing. As an example, if the volunteer fire departments, emergency services, or first aid groups do not have sufficient volunteer manpower or equipment for full service, the approval of additional housing projects in the area would magnify the problem. The tax consequences of going from volunteer to paid services would pose a political problem for the local planning/zoning boards. If the project is caught in the middle of this political dilemma, the government's inability to resolve the issue may result in the failure of the project. Knowing the issues and having a possible answer to the problem before the board presentation will further dissolve the political issues and possibly avert any delays.

The housing industry is complex because it is regulated by grassroots governmental agencies and political parties. The technical compliance for single-family subdivision design is generally a clear-cut, black-and-white issue. Differences in engineering approaches may be the only debate requiring a compromise in the approval process. It is the local, regional, state, and federal political arenas that influence the subdivision design characteristics beyond the technical parameters guiding infrastructure design. The best way to understand the political atmosphere or environment is to get to know the regulatory staff and the power base of the planning board. The staff will be able to outline the pros and cons of a proposed housing development. They can also define the political agenda and identify what the community is requiring of new housing projects during the approval process. New housing projects have been and will continue to be a conduit to improve or replace outdated community-owned infrastructure.

Know Your Costs ... Know What You Can Afford to Give Up

Local communities cannot always afford to upgrade existing infrastructure to accommodate housing growth. Thus, communities ask new housing projects to assist in a fair-share approach for improving infrastructure in and around the new housing project. The mechanism to gain this development support is through the planning board process. Many times, these issues are not included in discussions with staff members but are a result of the political review of the project. All project costs must be well defined, contingencies established, soft costs budgeted, and profit margin objectives maintained in creating the project pro forma, because of the effect politics has on housing projects.

Project presentations before planning boards are the forum in which developers are requested to provide construction or financial assistance toward the upgrading of existing infrastructure. At that moment, a decision must be made before the planning board as to whether to provide assistance or to debate the issues and seek relief from their demands. If the project costs are known, the decision can be made based on the financial facts of the project. Knowing the cost of offsite improvements, that is, road widening, drainage facilities, street lights, etc., is essential to render a decision before the planning board. The legal costs and delays versus the costs of site improvements need to be weighed. There are no winners in legal confrontation at the planning board table. If the project can afford to resolve the issue, a compromise is the best solution.

Planning Board Presentations

The approval of a project is contingent on the ability of the builder/developer or design team consultants to answer questions under the scrutiny of each planning board member, neighborhood group, and general audience. Prepare outlines for each presentation and orchestrate the design professionals in order to present the project in a logical and concise manner. Answering all of the questions, asked and not asked, of the design team during the presentation will make a positive impression on the planning board. Controversial issues need to be resolved outside of a public hearing. Minor issues can be resolved during the presentation and entered into the record.

Any time there is an issue discussed in the public forum that cannot be satisfactorily resolved by the design team, the audience and adversarial groups voicing objections to the project can benefit. As a result of this action, the planning board members would be put in a political dilemma, the staff members put in a questionable approval position, and the design professionals put in a compromising situation. Most likely, the approval will be delayed until all outstanding issues are resolved.

A planning board presentation strategy is successful when the project obtains approvals and construction can commence without delays. A successful strategy can be used to overcome delay in the public sector. In most states, a delay at a public meeting because of unresolved issues could effectively delay the project by 1 month. A 1-month delay may change the project schedule by more than 1 month. Any political delay would put the project in jeopardy if circumstances, such as site conditions, weather conditions, etc., would affect the start of the project once the issues were resolved.

Role-Playing

Two weeks before the planning board, board of adjustment, or council public meetings, schedule a meeting with the design team to present the project specifics before a select audience. Each presentation should be specific, to the point, and easy to understand. At this meeting, select the members who will present the project parameters in a style that would not be considered adversarial or condescending. During each presentation, the client should act as the mayor of the town and seriously guide the role-playing scenario. Role-playing should be as real as possible. The "mayor" should challenge all issues. Challenge the experts to think on their feet and to concisely answer all questions asked. Have several other staff members attend and ask specific controversial questions to all presenters.

This format energizes the design professional into a mental state of readiness, and it also achieves nonbiased discussions on any issue that may be lingering in the political arena. All issues that would have an adverse effect on the project approval should be discussed at length. During this role-playing, the design team should present their roles with the use of visual exhibits. Judge their approach, style, and content against the goals established for the project. All design team members should answer questions in a concise manner. Do not offer more than is required to answer the question. Know what your design team will say, when they will say it, and why they will say it. Conclude the presentation with corporate positions on issues that could be raised at the planning board meeting. All issues resolved during the presentation will help achieve a successful affirmative vote.

Planning Board Meeting

Schedule the design team to participate in a dinner meeting 2 to 3 hours before the planning board meeting. This will permit everyone to focus on the task at hand for that evening. Discuss any last-minute strategies or issues that might surface during the presentation and public session. All handouts and exhibits must be available at the dinner meeting. This dinner meeting format provides an environment for any last-minute debate of issues. The debate on issues must be openly expressed and discussed at length. However, once the decision is made on how to handle each specific issue, the design team must adhere to the consensus of the group. A united professional team that believes in the project provides positive emotion that will translate into momentum for the project.

ENGINEERS AT THE CROSSROADS

The engineering community associated with the housing industry is certainly at the crossroads. It is the crossroads of providing infrastructure design to protect the health, safety, and welfare of future homebuyers and of balancing the cost effectiveness of those design elements. If the cost does not justify the benefit to society, the engineering community must counteract overregulation.

When governmental engineers require infrastructure that is conservatively designed, the cost of developing land increases, and this cost is passed on to the consumer. Higher-priced homes and homeowner responsibilities for infrastructure maintenance are a direct result of a local government that dictates excessive standards without accepting the consequences. As an example, privately owned stormwater management facilities in a single-family subdivision will require CCRs governing that facility. There is a cost associated with the maintenance of the facility and with the enforcement of the regulations. This cost is in addition to the costs of purchasing a home. Many excessive regulations add to the constant monthly cost of operating a home. This is a direct result of local municipal governments continuing to shift community growth issues and passing the cost of the solutions on to the new homebuyer.

It is the engineering community that can directly affect the way housing developments are designed in the future. All residential design engineers should use design standards that are practical and cost effective. Use standards that justify the housing project intent regardless of the consistency with written governmental standards. There continues to be a regulatory effort to correct residential infrastructure operational problems with an expanded conservative design approach. Roadways seem to get wider, drainage pipes seem to get bigger, and design storm events seem conservative (i.e., design of the storm drain system is based on a 25-year storm in lieu of the standard 10-year storm). Public and private engineering firms must reach a middle ground on design issues. The housing industry is the only industry that hires an engineer to design a subdivision and hires another engineer to review the design. Engineers must use available information and documentation to eliminate duplicate review and approval processes. No other profession requires such a high level of professional judgment.

All of these issues in residential land development can be influenced by the civil engineering community. The decision is whether the engineering community will seek ways to provide quality living environments at reasonable costs or the conservative engineering design approach will outweigh the practical aspects of developing property. The engineering community is involved in the design, review, and approval of all subdivision projects. The engineering community can develop guidelines for future housing project designs that are ownership driven and not driven by political judgment.

COMMUNITY RELATIONS

All housing projects should extend beyond the two-dimensional design of the project. Builder/developers need to investigate and initiate community relations programs that create strategies necessary to obtain residential development approvals. A community relations program will maximize the support from elected officials and business leaders for the project. This type of program can be accomplished through the following methods:

1. The use of nonmedia communications, such as letters, community meetings, flyers, and introductory material for the community as a whole
2. A low-key neighbor-to-neighbor public relations program seeking feedback from residents neighboring the project so they become part of the design and not part of the problem

It is advantageous and always easier to educate the community on a neighbor-to-neighbor level so that the education process can be conveyed in a forum conducive to an excellent exchange of ideas. A sense of cooperation in educating the public will be effective. However, caution is necessary if the public relations campaign goes beyond reason. This will cause the audience to be more skeptical of the project itself.

Keeping an open line of communications with community leaders and elected officials is crucial to the success of the project. The selection of a staff member or the owner of the company as the contact person elevates the importance of the project, and this makes a proactive statement to the community. Any presentation before the community should be concise, on track, and meaningful in substance. All public campaigns must address the town's concerns and issues so that a sense of positive momentum can be achieved before the planning board hearing.

Strategic distribution of printed information to the local media, whether print or television, is an appropriate way to disseminate information to dispel any community rumors about the project. This should be done only after, and used to complement, scheduled meetings with neighbors, elected officials, and community leaders.

If the property and project become controversial, it would be recommended to create an advisory group with the town leaders as members. The chairman might be a local business person, mayor, former town council person, or a civic leader. The advisory group would become a third-party endorsement of the project. Constituents would listen to their point of view during the regulatory process. This advisory committee would be charged with the goal of disseminating project information in a proper forum.

Photo 10-1. Community Involvement. Developers of new housing projects should seek involvement from adjacent neighbors and the community. The consensus approval process is designed to address public concerns. It is rare that an advocate of a new housing project appears publicly to support the need for more housing.

As with any business, the builder/developer should establish a presence in the community by being involved in the events of the community. Donating time, effort, and resources to the betterment of the community will enhance the reputation of the firm and provide positive momentum. Community relations programs will succeed by striking a balance between art and science. The more positive attention the community receives as a whole, the more likely assistance will be given in obtaining an approval of the project.

TEN RULES FOR SUCCESS AT PLANNING BOARD HEARINGS

Rule 1—Know the Political "Hot Buttons"

Local politics control the development process. Every community has several key political "hot buttons" that govern the actions of the elected officials. It could be no growth, overcrowded schools, lack of volunteer firefighters, lack of affordable housing, environmental issues, etc. The list goes on and on. These hot buttons may change, but the old issues never fade away. The obvious hot buttons must be addressed in your project plans. The hot buttons you must know are the most current issues affecting your community at the time your project is being heard by the planning board.

The successful developer will answer all questions raised at the planning board and obtain a positive decision at the very first meeting. If there is an unforeseen hot button issue that had not been contemplated by the builder/developer and had not been resolved before the meeting, the project will be delayed at least 1 month or perhaps even longer.

How do you find out about the issues? Political involvement at the local level may be necessary. Join the Chamber of Commerce or become politically active. Stay involved at the local level by talking with the staff, board members, and politically active residents. The staff members assigned to the project are responsible for implementing the hot button issues and bringing the issues to the forefront of discussions with the applicant. Become professionally attuned to the requirements of the staff. Understand the political emphasis by local government at the time your project is being reviewed. Without question, the community hot buttons are a cost implication to the project and perhaps may even delay the project. Address the hot button issues before the issues are raised in a public forum.

Should you meet with board members? In the perfect world, reviewing the project with board members ahead of time would be an excellent way to inform them of the project specifics and have them better understand the approach to the project and the design emphasis, benefits, and positive implications of the project on the community. However, there are many locales where meeting with board members is not the proper approach because the general public would question the ethics, especially in a highly charged political arena. The best regulatory process implemented at the local level is a site plan review committee or a development review committee, which permits the staff members and selected planning board members to meet on a regular basis with builder/developers and their engineers on upcoming projects. It is an informal hearing in which the project can be discussed in a casual atmosphere and the board members and staff can voice their opinions. Most projects can be modified to meet the concerns raised at the informal hearing. Gaining immediate feedback on the project design and project issues is important so that all issues can be addressed before the public hearing.

Should the engineer become politically involved? A revenue source for engineering firms can come from being a municipal engineer, designing public works projects, or being retained to review projects by private developers. The municipal services provided by an engineering firm are somewhat recession-proof and are an excellent addition to any business plan. In some locations, in order to obtain this role, engineers have to become politically involved. Engineers can stay at arm's length from the political arena and allow the technical design be judged on its own merits. The best practice is to keep the engineering aspects of the land development business technical in nature and without political influence, if possible!

Rule 2—Public Participation has Become Unmanageable

Dealing with the general public during public participation at planning board meetings has become much more difficult and will only increase in difficulty as growth patterns increase. Only in the building business is profitability directly influenced by the general public. The system allows public input and public scrutiny for every project. Planning board members, all too often, consider the public views to be correct, and the development industry must prove the design approach is proper. It has become increasingly important, regardless of the size of the project, for engineers and their clients to reach out to neighborhoods and adjacent property owners to present the project prior to a board meeting.

Gaining neighborhood input before a planning board hearing is advantageous because it provides insight on what their problems and concerns are with the project. Project supporters may also be discovered! This approach would also provide the opportunity to address the public concerns before the public debate. It is better to stand before the planning board and tell them that meetings were held with the neighbors to explain the project. Most likely, the neighborhood views and the views of the builder/developer are not going to be consistent. It is vitally important to the success of the project to publicly declare that the public input has been taken into consideration in the development of the project. Most public hearings are not a positive environment in which to review plans in detail. The reaction from most public forums is a negative approach to the project simply because it is not always possible to have a project that does not require regulatory concessions. After all, the regulations are most often drafted in a vacuum.

If the project is of significant size, it will have a physical effect on the community, and will perhaps strain community services, such as the fire department, emergency response, police, schools, etc., then a positive public relations approach may also be necessary. This public relations program would consist of positive advertisements and media outreach to "spin" the positive aspects of the project. It would be important to illustrate the positive ramifications a project would have on the community as a whole. This public relations program would also include public participation in small neighborhood meetings. Engineers need to design projects that are technically acceptable by the regulatory engineer and can be publicly supported by the planning board.

The rule is always to consider the local neighbors and adjacent property owners' views and to gain their input before a public planning board hearing. The project will be viewed more favorably by the planning board members if your outreach program was sincere. Also, the public input portion of the hearing would be defused by addressing those public concerns during the presentation.

Rule 3—Know Your Costs

If the costs are not known before a hearing, it is difficult to know what to give up or compromise when asked by the planning board members. Knowing the cost of development provides the key decision element in making sound business and political judgments at the moment planning board members are seeking concessions or a compromise on the project. Any decision to comply with a planning board request will affect the cost of the project. If you do not know your costs and respond by saying, "I have to check." or "We will get back to you on that." you will be delayed at least 1 month, and time is money. Every hot button in a community has cost ramifications. Knowing the hot buttons and the costs associated with the hot buttons allows the board and builder/developer to reach an agreement in a public forum after constructive debate and concessions at the time of the meeting. If the issues could not be addressed before the meeting, resolving hot buttons or issues of public concern during the meeting will cause the project to remain on schedule, and unusual or undue delays are avoided.

Engineers should provide a detailed cost estimate of the project infrastructure at the preliminary plan stage. This allows the builder/developer to analyze the cash flow requirements and to make an assessment of the project viability before seeking final approvals. Regulatory standards governing the engineering design are not flexible, and changing the engineering design after the preliminary design is complete will not result in significant cost reductions in the infrastructure. Engineers affect the costs of a subdivision project on a daily basis and directly influence the profitability of the company. The job of the engineer is to make the builder/developer succeed in a project. Adding a buildable lot, reducing infrastructure costs, or expediting the plan production or regulatory approval process will all have a positive financial effect on the project.

Rule 4—Prepare For a Board Hearing

To properly prepare for a planning board hearing, engineers should know what the community hot buttons are, understand the project costs, and talk to the neighbors. Engineers must become familiar with the operation of each community's planning board staff and how the board functions to avoid surprises on the night of the meeting.

Engineers presenting a project before a planning board should become familiar with:

1. The hearing room layout
2. Where the board members, audience, and presenter are situated in the room
3. How the exhibit will be situated in the room for presentation
4. The acoustics of the room and if a microphone is used
5. The availability of an easel or a computer for graphics

Always repeat questions so that the entire audience can hear the questions and the answers. Every jurisdiction is slightly different in the way it processes plans, reviews plans, and debates the designs. Engineers must understand the nuances of each community in which they work. Builder/developers will retain those engineers who understand their communities the best. Engineers should establish themselves as the most knowledgeable of a jurisdiction and establish connections to the staff and politicians so the client base has no other choice but to select them.

Rule 5—Prepare Quality Graphics

Most presenters fail to use exceptional color graphics to illustrate the characteristics of the project. Clearly, computer-generated graphics that can be displayed by the computer at planning board hearings are more available. Certainly the more sophisticated or advanced the planning board, the easier it is to display the specifics of the project through computer presentations. Appropriately colored exhibits are just as important as the presentation. The illustration of a project elevates the professionalism of the design team members and demands a higher level of attention and understanding by the planning board members and the general public. Engineers must learn styles of illustration or have a staff member with artistic talent prepare the presentation material.

Rule 6—Use Appropriate Tools of the Trade

To prepare for a planning board hearing, the design team should practice their presentations by role-playing. The project may be of such importance or controversy that written scripts may be necessary. The written scripts should include anticipated questions and prepared answers. Certainly, do not leave the presentation to be ad libbed. Make sure the message is well thought out and well presented. Role-playing allows the design team members an opportunity to critique the presentation and ask difficult questions about the project. Practice answering difficult questions in a positive and upbeat manner.

It is best when notes are not used during the presentation, but have project material at your fingertips, if needed. Always arrive at the hearing ahead of time and review the agenda to determine if the position is favorable. Successful professional consultants can explain a technical subject in lay terms. Most planning board members and the general public are not trained in reading construction drawings. They will primarily address emotional and political issues that affect the community. It is incumbent on all engineering firms to train their young engineers in the art of presenting a technical project before a planning board in an environment that could be hostile, adversarial, and stressful. Builders and developers should be willing to mentor and encourage young engineers to represent them before a public body. The client will usually allow it if the engineering firm gives the young engineer the opportunity. Otherwise, the client will use only the experienced presenter to obtain approvals.

Rule 7—Orchestrate the Performance

As the size of the project increases in the number of housing units, orchestrating the planning board performance for the design team becomes more important. The attorney and client are key members of the design team. A determination should be made as to their role in the presentation. There are many builder/developers who present their own projects, and engineers are called on only for technical support. In most jurisdictions, the engineer is the primary presenter of a subdivision project, and the client is there in a support role for decision-making purposes. The design team members should arrive before the meeting starts with all graphics. The order of the presentation will have already been determined. Keep the presentation as brief as possible. The last presenter should be the presenter of the "sizzle." This ends a presentation on a subject matter that all can relate to and can feel good about (i.e., landscaping, architecture, colors, environmental sensitivity, amenities). The larger the project, in terms of the number of units and effect on a community, the more important the order of your design team consulting group becomes in terms of how your story is presented to the planning board. The sizzle can sell the project to the board members.

Rule 8—Present a Project with Enthusiasm

It is good to show enthusiasm for the project design. In fact, most engineers are so intimately and emotionally involved in the design of a subdivision that they can easily take exception to criticism and critique of the project. Keeping discussions professional and impersonal will best serve the engineer at the planning board podium. Display positive enthusiasm and humanize the project. This will soften the technical characteristics of the project and be better received by the public and board members. This will help establish your credibility and have the audience view the project much more positively. Be genuine and sincere in the presentation and the message. Be enthusiastic and professional.

There are very few occasions when a presenter must show anger during a presentation or during a question-and-answer session. These rare occasions are precipitated by a project being judged politically rather than on its technical merits. But 99.9% of the time, showing anger at a planning board hearing is not warranted, and all credibility will be lost. It is not in the best interest of the project nor in the best interest of the presenter to ever lose their temper in a public forum. Do not show distress or nervousness in your voice, and certainly do not display arrogance. Local approvals allow all input from all people, so the engineer must regard all the input with a high degree of professionalism. Success at the planning board meeting hinges on the ability to present the project in a distinctly professional manner with a foundation of enthusiasm.

Rule 9—Answer Questions Briefly

Engineers should consider a planning board hearing as a court of law. Thus, the engineer should tailor the presentation and answers as if giving a deposition. If an answer demands a yes or no answer, the design team member should answer yes or no and not elaborate or explain the answer. To elaborate would only give the audience and planning board members an opportunity to think of more questions. Always repeat the question so that everyone hears the question and that the question has been interpreted correctly. The most important period during the hearing is when the public is permitted to ask questions. It is important for the design team professionals answering questions to be highly respectful and show sincere interest in the public comments and questions. The ability to answer the questions and have the public feel good about the answer is an art that comes only with practice, practice, practice. Because many planning board members react to the reaction of the general public, the design team members must maintain a positive framework in which to answer questions.

A negative and adversarial audience causes the project to be more controversial, and the planning board members will be less likely to embrace the project for its positive contributions to the community. The presenter must diffuse the adverse public attitude before the meeting, during the presentation, and during the question-and-answer session.

Rule 10—Pass the Torch

Engineering firms should implement an in-house program for the training of young engineers in the art of planning board presentations. Most engineering students coming out of college are not trained in giving speeches, especially not at an adversarial planning board. Engineering firms should consider the following training program:

1. Have the young professionals take a speech class, such as Toastmasters or Dale Carnegie.
2. Develop an in-house speaking forum for the young engineers to present a project to other staff members in a role-playing atmosphere. The role-playing should include an intensive question-and-answer period.
3. Young professionals should attend planning board meetings to get a feel for the action and experience the way meetings are organized. Have the young engineer attend a planning board hearing on a controversial project and attend every meeting on that controversial project until a vote is rendered.
4. Have the young professional present a small non-controversial project before a planning board.
5. Train the young professional to easily relate to people in the art of planning board presentations and public participation programs by having them present a technical subject in lay terms.

A methodical training program will allow young engineers to progress more rapidly and better serve the client base in and out of the planning board hearing room.

CHAPTER 11

Permits ... Permits

COMMUNITY INVOLVEMENT

The housing industry is one of the most highly regulated industries by all levels of government. Each housing project has to obtain various permits and approvals from local, state, regional, and federal government agencies before construction. The housing industry is the only industry in which the community and the public, as a whole, can influence the design and approval of the housing project. The general public, by objecting to a proposed residential project, can affect the approval process and the business success of a development firm.

Many municipal planning boards are political appointees, which should cater to the public. It is the position of planning boards to achieve a consensus of opinion before a project can be approved. The developer's design team must present the positive attributes of the project in order to persuade the board to vote affirmatively for the project. Large projects generally gain more public attention, and with it more objections will be raised—founded or unfounded. The planning board members must objectively review both sides of the case and decide what's best for the community. Unfortunately, those people in need of a new home generally become knowledgeable of a project only after the sales office opens for sales. During the regulatory process, the buyers in the housing market do not know of upcoming projects and therefore are unable to have the opportunity to voice their opinion.

As the no-growth environment continues to spread and regulations expand, it will become more difficult for large housing projects to gain approvals. The cost for the design team will be substantial. This will encourage the development of smaller multiple sites in noncompeting locations to satisfy different segments of the housing market. A successful approval process and planning board hearing are contingent on the knowledge and persuasive capabilities of the design team. Their knowledge of the regulations implemented to govern land use and development ordinances must be impeccable to achieve success. Builder/developers, however, cannot rely solely on the design team to look out for their best interest. The owner, or delegated staff members, must become more aware of the regulations that affect the building community. In the development business, they must guide and lead the design team to an all-win attitude at the planning table.

The regulations implementing planning and zoning ordinances change through the interpretation of those regulations by staff members. It is this interpretation that causes an uneven playing field for those developers competing in the same marketplace. If the preferences and interpretations differ from reviewer to reviewer, the regulatory review and approval will differ from project to project.

As the regulations are implemented, the cost of land development will increase. Most communities act on the side of conservatism, which translates into higher costs. If the governmental reviews are not consistent with the regulations, an imbalance in the housing marketplace will ultimately cause the approval process to be governed by politics.

LOCAL GOVERNMENTS

Local governments favor housing projects consistent with their master plans and land use regulations. A proposed housing project consistent with the zoning ordinance will be reviewed by the planning board. The board of adjustment acts on projects seeking relief from the zoning regulations. Designing the project without requesting approval for design waivers and variances will increase chances of success at the planning board. An excellent trial balloon for a project is the conceptual site plan review process, which is an open exchange of views between the developer, regulatory staff, and politicians. The views are not binding on any party. It is the preliminary and final plan reviews that affect the project design parameters. All projects should be presented in a positive manner knowing that the project will not become a reality until the final subdivision map or plat has been approved for recordation.

PLANNING BOARD

The planning board is the primary legal government agency that manages the development process. All other agencies support the planning board and are charged to provide specialized expertise in reviewing subdivision proposals. Each jurisdiction will have various community interest groups influencing the subdivision process.

AGENCIES

These agencies should review the project plans and determine the effect the project will have on public services.

Photo 11-1. Subdivisions for Vehicles. Many communities have approached housing projects with the opinion that neighborhoods should be designed for vehicle movement, access, and maintenance.

Shade Tree Commission

This citizen group reviews housing projects for their effect on existing trees. Shade tree commissions are charged to manage and protect existing trees and enhance community beautification. This commission will also review housing projects for compliance with landscaping, tree preservation, and reforestation regulations.

Environmental Commission

Many local governments have created environmental commissions to review design plans for endangered species, endangered vegetation, and wetlands. All environmental concerns that may affect the project are duly considered during the review process. In most cases, the environmental commission consists of politically appointed people having a sincere interest in protecting the environment from the construction of new housing projects. The local environmental movement becomes much more vocal and much more intense during the review process. The environmental commission highlights problem areas and leaves the solutions up to the design team. Developers should welcome input from the commission to find ways and methodologies for subdivision designs to complement the environment.

Photo 11-2. Subdivisions for People. Housing subdivisions should be designed for the land, homes, and people. Developers should approach a design with creativity and work within the regulatory framework for the necessary approvals and permits.

Water and Sewer Departments

Community water and sewer facilities fall under the jurisdiction of either a separate municipal utility authority or the public works department. The design of water and sewer facilities for a residential subdivision is reviewed by regulatory engineers at the local and state levels. In many cases, the utility design review has a separate time schedule from the planning board process. As long as there are water and sewer available, jurisdictions will approve a subdivision, subject to the utilities being approved by the appropriate government agency. In some communities, the local utility design is subject to county, regional, and state approvals.

Drainage Departments

Storm drainage facilities for residential subdivisions are generally reviewed and approved by the public works department, or, in some cases, an outside consulting engineering firm is retained to review the engineering design work. The implementation of the local drainage ordinance will vary from one engineer to the next. Knowing the reviewer and their preferences in drainage design is important for achieving approval during the initial plan submission.

Photo 11-3. Water and Sewer Facilities. The availability and capacity of existing water and sewer facilities continue to guide residential growth patterns. In-fill or overlooked sites can be creatively designed for residential uses and can be cost effective because of the availability of existing infrastructure.

Traffic Departments

Communities may also have traffic districts or transportation districts to evaluate the effect of the traffic generated from the proposed subdivision. This agency would concentrate on adjacent existing roadways and intersections. In many growth areas, local government strives to implement taxing districts or assess impact fees against the housing project for its fair share of public improvement projects. Unfortunately, the assessment of fees and the transfer of community responsibility onto the new homebuyer have resulted in higher prices for homes in those areas.

Project Reviews

The project improvement plans could be reviewed by up to seven consulting engineers who have varying backgrounds and represent all levels of government. These engineers review, approve, reject, and/or revise the design intent of the project.

Once a final plat is approved, municipal governments may require a performance bond or a letter of credit for the subdivision to be posted at 120% of the improvement cost. Also, an inspection fee may be assessed so that the consulting engineering firm representing the government can inspect the project during construction and during the maintenance bond period. For any subdivision, regardless of the size, the land plan should be evaluated for phasing. Phasing will conserve the cash flow to build the project and achieve maintenance bond status in a shorter period of time. The primary objective of land development operations is to build the improvements with high-quality workmanship in order to gain maintenance bond status as quickly as possible. This approach will limit the project liability for the infrastructure and begin to establish the responsibility for the operation and maintenance of the infrastructure with the local government.

Most municipal engineers prepare bond estimates using inflated unit prices. These costs are generally much higher than private industry prices established during the bid process. Serious discussions should be initiated if the bond estimates are extremely high. Limiting the problems at the performance bond stage will help the overall corporate financial position on the project. A favorable bond estimate may assist in using the additional financial resources or bonding limits for subsequent project phases or housing projects.

Regional Agencies

Cities or incorporated towns may have their own planning boards. In addition, there may be a county planning board, which oversees county-owned roadways but also approves the subdivision plan. This layer of government review is not uncommon, and each housing project is subjected to another review by engineers and another layer of political scrutiny.

The soil conservation district, in most states, is a regional agency that governs the review and approval of sedimentation and erosion control design measures for residential projects. This agency governs all soil disturbance activities. Residential project submission and review fees sustain the district's budget. The soil conservation district's review process has a separate regulatory approval time frame. It is common for the regulations of the soil conservation district to be in conflict and expand the regulations imposed by local, regional, and state agencies. At times, a developer may be caught in the middle between agencies. This regulatory conflict will delay the approval of the project unless the art of negotiation and compromise can be used with the different agencies. This situation is damaging to a project schedule, and direct management of the situation is required by the builder/developer.

Some states have regional stormwater or river basin agencies responsible for reviewing residential storm drainage designs to determine the effect the project will have on major streams, rivers, or other bodies of water. Review fees, application fees, and the approval process are separate from the local approval procedure. In some states, stormwater management facilities may be regulated by four to five government agencies. The duplicated, conflicting, and excessive regulations governing residential storm drainage design adds to the cost of homes and delays the approval process.

Some states have regional groups established through legislation that govern large areas for protection, enhancement, and proper use. This regional agency

Photo 11-4. Permits, Permits, Permits. Residential housing projects are subjected to multiple governmental reviews and permit approvals. Agencies at the local, county, regional, state, and federal levels will be involved in the approval of a housing project.

structure is layered over other local, regional, and state approvals. As an example, in New Jersey, the Pinelands Commission is responsible for the overall development and land use of the National Pinelands Area. The Pinelands Commission approval process is complex, time consuming, and very expensive. The Pinelands Commission has its own regulations, which, in most cases, are much more restrictive than other agencies involved in the overseeing of residential development. Also in New Jersey, as well as in other states, there are agencies that review housing developments located near the ocean.

Having several small projects at different levels of approval or construction would permit financial cash flow of the business to be properly managed. The phasing of projects in areas that are not governed by a regional agency will obviously provide an easier path to the building and selling of lots and houses. Locating projects within several political jurisdictions with varying approval processes is a business plan designed to earn a profit, generate business, establish an employment base, and maintain a corporate presence in the community. Having several small projects will reduce the risk factor, and the business growth goals can be achieved, even if one project is delayed.

There are other regional agencies that are quasipublic, such as the telephone, electric, gas, and cable companies. These companies will also review the con-

Photo 11-5. Alternative Technology. If public water and sewer facilities are not available to the project site, investigate the many alternative methods of providing utility service.

struction drawings of the subdivision. The underground utility layout will be based on the engineering design plans. In some cases, the utility design will not complement or be coordinated with the design of the subdivision. The utility company may locate structures along common property lines at the right-of-way line. Thus, the project engineer should evaluate the location of driveways, storm drain inlets, manholes, and yard swales that may be in conflict with utility company transformers, cable boxes, telephone poles, etc. If there should be a conflict, the engineering plans should be revised to complement the utility company design for the project. If the change can be made without disrupting the project, change the plans. Changing the utility company's design will take longer to accomplish.

State Agencies

States oversee the implementation of housing master plans within the political subdivisions of the state and evaluate the effect housing has on the state's natural resources. States emphasize the protection of the environmental attributes of the state, such as wetlands. Some states have exceeded federal wetlands-mandated guidelines and have expanded their role in the protection of wetlands within the state boundaries. States will control state waters and the effect development has on this resource.

States may also have specific endangered species and endangered plant lists that need to be considered during the site analysis review. These sensitive environmental issues can be used as a benefit to the project. The environmental attributes of the site can be positive marketing images. Most states approve water and sewer public facilities. States allocate utility permits for water and sewer facilities by using existing infrastructure to guide community growth. Areas outside of the public service areas would have to use alternative methods of providing water and sewer facilities. These alternative methods, such as septic systems, can also be managed by state agencies. Individual wells providing potable water to each dwelling are permitted by state agencies. States will monitor and manage the drawdown of aquifers caused by multiple individual wells or by expansion of public facilities serving new housing developments.

State-mandated building codes based on the model building codes are implemented through state agencies but controlled and managed by local building departments. These code provisions also affect the way subdivisions are designed.

Federal Government

Several federal agencies—the departments of housing and urban development, energy, and environmental protection—have a direct effect on housing projects and the use of land for developments. Federal agencies are responsible for the protection of endangered species and endangered plants listed on the federal registry. The Corps of Engineers has regulated wetlands and flood plain areas for many years. Some states have taken over the jurisdiction of the implementation of wetland protection. Since the passage of the Clean Water Act, the regulation of stormwater, wetland, and environmental issues for subdivisions has been elevated to a much higher plateau of sensitivity. Another federal agency having an effect on development operations is the Occupational Safety and Health Administration (OSHA).

SUBDIVISION APPROVAL PROCESS

A typical subdivision approval process, from inception to final approval, illustrates the various levels through which any housing project will most likely be processed. This approval process does not clearly indicate the amount of work and effort that private industry must accomplish over and above what is shown on this chart, just to obtain market acceptance.

Before the subdivision process starts, a tremendous amount of investigative work, contract negotiations, and value judgment have to be made before financial resources are allocated for the submission of improvement plans. After completing the regulatory process and obtaining governmental approvals, the marketability, success, or failure of a project will not be known until model homes are constructed. The public will be the entity that judges the marketability of the product because they will look and buy or just look!

Typically, it can take from 1.5 to 2.5 years from finding land to giving the keys to the first homeowner. In some states, the ability to close a home will take less time and less financial resources to complete a project. However, in many states, the regulatory process continues to be more complex and more layered, so the development industry is viewed as a high-risk industry in which success is earned. The philosophy of developing small parcels for a relatively small number of homes, even up to 50 houses or 50 lots, would provide an excellent inventory of approved and unimproved land. The financial resources to build out and to sell out a subdivision of up to 50 lots can be managed by many small- to medium-sized development firms or building companies.

Government reviews and approvals and the issuance of permits are imbedded in the bureaucracy to control the development pattern of a community. In fact, many processes will continue to evolve as special interest groups lobby government to influence the development process. The success of the industry rests on the shoulders of those who understand and seek solutions within the framework of government regulations.

PLANNING BOARD GUIDE FOR CITIZEN PARTICIPATION

The regulatory climate and atmosphere are driven by four elements:

1. Planning board members
2. Municipal professional staff members
3. Applicants and their design team members
4. Members of the general public

Most planning boards encourage and welcome citizen input at planning board hearings. In fact, public comment sessions, including question-and-answer periods for the general audience, are commonplace. Unfortunately, most municipal government do not really inform the citizenry of the proper hearing procedures and laws that govern planning board operations and management responsibilities.

Engineering firms should prepare a citizens' guide to planning board hearings and make the brochure available at the planning board hearings. This brochure would be for the general public to read and understand before and during the meeting. If an engineering firm wanted to work with its local planning board, the following segments of a brochure could be the basis on which a brochure could be prepared for public distribution:

1. The application process should define some of the major elements of a housing, commercial, or industrial project that are reviewed and approved by planning boards. These applications would include such definitions as site plans, minor and major subdivisions, master plans, or concept plans that might be included on a planning board agenda. A description of each appli-

cation type would be appropriate, but also include other governmental agencies required to review each type of application.

2. The brochure should include the role each agency has in the subdivision approval process. Provide contact names and phone numbers for all of the agencies involved, including governmental departments such as the engineering department, the fire safety department, the traffic safety department, the planning department, environmental commissions, shade tree commissions, water and sewer districts, soil conservation districts, and other utility companies—gas, electric, telephone, and cable companies.

3. The brochure should outline the exact procedure in which the municipal government reviews subdivision applications. As an example, the applicant submits a certain number of plans, applications, and fees associated with a subdivision plan. The package is submitted to the planning board secretary 10 to 14 days before the next regularly scheduled planning board meeting. The application is reviewed for completeness to ensure that all of the information is contained in the submission. Once the application has been deemed complete, an explanation of the distribution of the plans should be outlined in detail. The time permitted for the review by each agency should be indicated. Information should be included in the brochure that states that all plans, reports, environmental impact studies, traffic studies, and drainage reports are made available at the planning board office during regular business hours for review by the general public. After the application has been deemed complete and reviewed by the governmental staff, the application is scheduled for a public hearing.

4. The brochure should describe the types of approvals rendered by the planning board, such as preliminary approval, final plat approval, or approval conditions. The brochure should include what days the planning board meets, what time the meeting starts, and what time the meeting is adjourned. The brochure should also indicate how the agenda is arranged, such as first-come first-served, or if the application has been delayed, postponed, or moved from one month to another because of legal notice problems, etc.

5. The list of the type of meetings should be defined. Many planning boards hold work sessions, informal hearings, and formal hearings. A flow chart illustrating the application process and the type of hearings would be easily understood by the general public.

6. What the public will witness at the public hearing should be outlined in the brochure. As an example, explain that there is a planning board secretary who keeps minutes, handwritten or by tape. There will be planning board officials, a planning board attorney, and professional staff members providing technical input and review documents. Also attending will be the applicants, design team members, attorneys, and the general public. Most meetings start with the Pledge of Allegiance, a reading of the previous meeting's minutes, an approval of invoices, the memorializing of previous resolutions,

and address of any issues or topics of interest, which may include master plan issues or ordinances. An explanation of each component of the agenda will help the audience understand the workings of a planning board hearing.

7. The brochure should include a section on the applicant's presentation and how the board interacts with the applicant and the design team members or expert witnesses. Clearly indicate for the public what to expect during the presentation and review of a specific application. The applicant is asked to present the project in a distinct and professional manner. The applicant will most likely be the builder or developer. They will have an attorney or their engineer present the project specifics. The engineer will most likely present the technical aspects of the project. The application must be presented methodically to illustrate how the project benefits the community as a whole. The intent of the project is outlined in detail, and what the public will expect once the project has been completed will be described.

    Once the presentation of the applicant is completed, the planning board members and agency professionals will have an opportunity to ask specific questions about the project design. The applicant will respond to each question in sufficient detail. If the question is phrased to allow a "yes" or a "no" answer, the applicant will generally respond in that fashion. The chairman of the planning board will keep the hearing running efficiently and will strive to keep the discussions on point, brief, and detailed as much as possible.

8. Once the board members and staff have completed their reviews and discussions, the chairman will open the public session for questions and answers. The brochure should include a list of "dos and don'ts" for the public to follow during the public portion of the presentation. Generally, the public forum will last as long as there are citizens willing to ask non-repetitive questions. The public session is for asking questions and not for making speeches. The chairman should not permit duplicate questions by the public. The public should maintain a sense of decorum regardless of the emotional aspects of the project. The chairman must keep control of the meeting and not permit unruly participation by either the applicant or the public.

9. The successful municipalities will have work sessions or workshops with the applicants to discuss a project design with several members of the planning board and staff. The forum is generally an informal discussion, and the opinions and discussions are nonbinding for the applicant.

10. The brochure could be expanded to include definitions of terms generally heard at planning board meetings (i.e., waivers, zoning ordinances, bulk requirements, resolutions, design exceptions, variances, and engineering terminology). The brochure could include the application forms and fee schedule that applicants have to complete before the project is accepted for review by the municipality. A planning board public awareness brochure would be welcomed by those individuals in the arena. When the public is informed of the process, they become part of the process and will respect the system and

the efforts of all parties involved. When all parties, including the general public, adhere to the rules of the planning board, the meetings and presentations will proceed efficiently and without undue interruptions. After all, time is money for the applicant, and any delay affects the success of the project.

CHAPTER 12

Land Development Bid Process

The bid process is the bridge between the approval process, regulatory approvals, and the construction of the project. This chapter discusses, in depth, a step-by-step procedure that provides residential land development methodology on how to know your costs, schedule the work properly, understand contractor capabilities, and construct a quality subdivision. This bid process can give the project the highest chance of achieving budget success and adherence to the project schedule.

PLANS AND SPECIFICATIONS

The construction documents amended during the final design phase of the regulatory permit process are approved as the final construction documents used to construct the subdivision. These construction documents, once approved, should be stamped for construction, dated as of the last revision date, and signed and sealed by the professional engineer in charge of the project. As owners, accept only design plans stamped "For Construction" for distribution to contractors. This documentation provides the contractors with the knowledge and comfort that the plans have received local governmental approvals.

Municipalities may require signature blocks on the construction documents for the planning board chairman, secretary, and municipal engineer. They would sign the original plans, indicating their approval of the construction documents. Even if a locale does not have this mechanism in place, it is a good idea to provide a signature block for future reference. This reference is especially important for when the municipality ultimately accepts ownership and maintenance of the project.

Residential subdivisions should have their own land development specifications, as outlined in Figure 12-1. This outline primarily indicates the various headings incorporated in the specifications report. Unlike specifications that relate to interstate highways or major public works programs, these specifications are consistent with the activities required to construct residential projects. The specifications are owner friendly and put most of the construction and design responsibilities and liabilities onto the appropriate parties. These specifications, if implemented in the field and monitored by the owner and the local municipality, provide a framework of building a quality subdivision. If there is interest in obtaining a complete specifications document, contact the author.

PREBID CONFERENCE WITH STAFF

Before sending the plans and specifications out for land development bid proposals, schedule a prebid conference with the operational staff responsible for overseeing the construction. A brief outline of the prebid conference is provided in Figure 12-2. The project specifics and construction requirements should be discussed in detail. Begin with clearing operations and follow through to the construction sequence of events. During the prebid conference with staff members, any problems associated with the construction documents and the adherence to project schedules should be outlined and discussed in depth.

If the project is to be phased, the location for the storage of materials, the staging areas for equipment, and the delivery of the first housing construction pad should be discussed. Land development activities for a residential project should complement the housing activities of the builder. A defined timetable and project schedules should be discussed to determine if there are any unusual hurdles or extenuating circumstances that may affect the schedule and the delivery of the first housing pad. The corporate objective is to deliver pads on schedule in order to sell lots or construct homes.

Discuss with the staff the recommendations on which contractors should be asked to bid on the project. Discuss the benefits of hiring separate contractors having specific expertise (such as utility installations, curbing, paving, etc.) versus hiring a contractor responsible for the entire project but who subcontracts out for specialty items. Hiring separate contractors for various activities can provide a lower overall project cost. However, this has to be weighed against having additional onsite supervision. Also, any failure of infrastructure will be debated as to the responsible party when multiple contractors may have caused the failure.

If the contractor retained to build the project subcontracts out the work, the owner should hold the contractor responsible for any failure to the infrastructure. In discussing available contractors, price is certainly a consideration, but the delivery of pads for housing construction generates the cashflow. The first-phase housing lots should be constructed on an expedited schedule. The design plans must be sensitive to the phasing objectives of the company. Once the first-phase pads have been constructed, the land development infrastructure must be completed to eliminate conflict with housing subcontractors. This allows closing of lots while subsequent phases are being constructed.

BID PROCESS

The contractors selected to bid on the project are contacted by phone or letter and asked if they would like to bid on certain activities or on the entire land development work. It is appropriate to charge a fee for the project plans given to contractors. This fee will defray the cost of printing the construction documents. The fee could also be considered a deposit if the plans are to be returned. All returned plans can always be used during the construction process.

Contractor Information

Each contractor should complete the contractor information sheet, as shown in Figure 12-3, and return the form with the bid proposal. This information sheet requests data on the financial capability of the firm and a list of references. These references should be contacted. Always consider new firms in order to expand the bid list. Most new firms are motivated do work on time and within budget. For new companies, check references and visually inspect their previous work. Also seek a personal commitment from the owners of the company to meet schedules and price agreements.

Contractor Meeting

Before the submission of bids by the contractors, a meeting with the contractors should be scheduled to present the project goals and objectives. This meeting is a joint meeting of all contractors asked to bid on the project. This meeting invites all of the contractors to see and hear their competition. It also permits an open discussion of the project specifics, which will only benefit the project. The contractors should have the construction documents at least 1 week before this general meeting. This allows them time to review, analyze, inspect, and understand the intent of the project. At the contractor meeting, discuss project details, scheduling, phasing, and design elements. In addition to the contractors present, invite local utility company representatives, municipal inspectors, the design engineer, and the project architect to attend this meeting. It gives everyone an opportunity to openly discuss the design specifics of the project and the construction requirements for delivering the first housing pad. There should be sufficient time for all of the contractors to ask specific questions.

This type of meeting allows the contractor sufficient time to fully comprehend the project parameters. Thus, during the analysis of the bids, discussions on any unknown or unusual factors should already have been addressed. It would therefore be reasonable to expect that all contractors submitting bids would fully understand the project details. The importance of having the competitors ask questions and face off with their counterparts is to ensure that potential problems are addressed before they become actual problems. Also, contractors will provide a very competitive price before entering into the negotiation phase because they know their competition.

Photo 12-1. Implementing the Design. The land development bid process should include an investigation of the contractor's capabilities, experience, and reputation in constructing residential subdivisions.

During the contractor meeting, establish clear timetables for the submission of bids. A defined deadline for the submission of bids is appropriate, and it should be stressed that any bid submitted after that date or specific time will not be accepted. The contractors should be involved in the setting the deadline. If the contractors do not meet the deadline, it is a clear indication of their inability to comply with a schedule and perhaps their inability to perform the land development activities.

Setting of a timetable is a method to judge someone's capability to live within a management framework before the commencement of construction. Schedules in land development and housing projects are the key to carrying out any successful project and to sustaining positive project cashflow. Builder/developers rely on contractors to perform efficiently, on time, within budget, and with a high degree of quality.

Contractor's Schedule

A builder/developer's reputation is either established or tarnished by contractors implementing construction documents in the field. The contractor should submit the project schedule with the bid proposal. This schedule will outline the elements of the work in a timeframe that can be analyzed against corporate goals for delivering houses for closing. The schedule is one aspect of a review of the contractor's manpower, quality of construction, reputation, and ability to perform in the field. Their schedule becomes their personal commitment to complete the work on time.

Bid Forms

Consider preparing bid forms for the contractors to use in submitting their prices. This bid form would show the various work activities. Either leave the unit quantities blank or provide the quantities in the bid form. In either case, the design engineer should be providing a detailed quantity report for the project using the same activities required of the land development contractors. The design engineer could provide unit pricing, but it is not necessary because the pricing is to be provided by the contractors for their specific work responsibilities.

By providing quantities in the bid form, the quantities supplied by each contractor can be compared in detail. Thus, it is easier to compare the individual bids to obtain a true comparison of costs. If the quantities are not included on the bid form, land development contractors will organize their bids by altering quantities and unit pricing to suit their operational style. They will also indicate any problems with the quantities. Also, this approach makes it very difficult for the owner to properly compare bids. This approach will require substantial discussions with all bidders to ensure the comparison of each proposal is completed with fairness.

Bid Analysis

On receipt of the bid proposals, use an accounting sheet or a computer software spreadsheet to enter in the quantities, unit prices, and total prices for each element of work. If the quantities are provided, the analysis is reduced to reviewing the unit pricing for each category. If the contractors do not alter the quantities, it can be concluded that the quantities are accurate. It is difficult to make a comparison of the work activities and prices among contractors. In most cases, the engineering company should have the capabilities to provide accurate cut-and-fill quantities for the project design. Most earthwork contractors are computerized to provide a printout of the cut-and-fill analysis for the project. This information would be reviewed against the quantities prepared by the engineers. If there are no discrepancies or debates over the quantities, the negotiation is centered on contractor pricing, scheduling, manpower, and experience.

Prepare a spreadsheet by using the contractor unit prices and extend the quantities to prepare a cost estimate for each land development activity. As in Figure 12-4, the bid analysis can be entered into the computer or simply be done by hand. On review of each bid proposal, the owner must resolve any bid discrepancies to ensure there is a true comparison among bid proposals. Any bid discrepancy, if significant, should be presented to all companies so there are no underlying problems during the analytical aspect of the project. Because this is a private contractual arrangement, public bidding laws do not have jurisdiction over the process. However, it is good business practice to ensure the bid comparisons are true comparisons to permit decisions to be made on a monetary basis and not on a personal basis.

After spreading the schedule of values, double check the unit prices, extensions, and any notations the contractor made to ensure that the contractor understands the scope of the work. If there seems to be a misunderstanding of the work scope highlighted in the bid proposal, the contractor should be contacted to resolve the misunderstanding.

Once the schedule of values has been extended and all discrepancies resolved, analyze each bid proposal and prepare a detailed recommendation on the contractor selection. Prepare negotiation strategies for each contractor selected to do the work.

CONTRACTOR SELECTION PROCESS

The following are key elements of the contractor selection process: competitive price, sense of cooperation, skill, expertise, project experience, reliability, references, professionalism of the owner and experienced management staff, quality equipment, and qualified superintendents. The contractor must have a qualified superintendent on the job site because the builder/developer will be working with them on a day-to-day basis. The superintendent must be sensitive to the owner's needs during construction. If the contractor's superintendent has been delegated the responsibility to build the project and his decisions are questionable, the contractor should be asked to assign someone different to manage the project.

If there are several contractors within a reasonable range of total dollars, those companies should be asked to proceed with the negotiation of a contract price. The intent is not to produce a bidding war, but it is incumbent on the builder/developer to get the best price for the work. There are contractors that may view the project as important to meet their corporate goals. They may be more willing to work with less of a profit margin just to get the work. Land developers need to keep their equipment and their workforce working on a continuous basis. The automatic selection of the low bidder may not be the appropriate action. It is appropriate to call two or three contractors to further negotiate the final contract agreement.

If separate contractors are being selected for different land development activities, such as for curb or paving work, the negotiations should be limited to the specific work items. The combined individual contractor prices should be compared to the general contractor's price to do all of the work under their corporate umbrella. This approach will provide a true comparison of the price for a group of individual contractors versus the price from one contractor. The cost difference has to be weighed against the management responsibility required to oversee multiple subcontractors.

If the bid proposal includes the owner's quantities, the unit prices for each activity require negotiation. Sometimes it is more cost effective to negotiate a lower price on a specific line item having a large quantity. The cost savings may be much greater than those achieved by concentrating on the negotiation of an unreasonable unit price for a small amount of work.

During the negotiation phase, meet with the contractors to discuss their bid proposals and obtain the personal commitment from each contractor to adhere to the project schedule. This personal commitment is important to the overall success of the project. A well-constructed project is hardly ever recognized by its quality but is judged by the number of complaints. Eliminating problems with strong management will be the only award a contractor will receive. If the project is critical to business objectives, provide a timetable with financial incentives to the contractor. If quality construction can be accelerated ahead of schedule, consideration should be given to providing a financial award to the contractor.

LAND DEVELOPMENT CONTRACTS

The preparation of a land development contract for execution by the owner and land development contractor can take several forms.

Unit Price Contract

This type of contract establishes specific unit prices for specific work scopes, and the quantities of material installed are measured in the field. The agreed-on unit prices would be used to calculate the ultimate payment for work accomplished.

Time and Material Contract

This contract is a labor, equipment, and material cost-based contract. The contractor should provide an equipment list and the hourly cost for equipment and labor (i.e., the equipment operator). The equipment time and material used would be the basis of the contract. Generally, in a time and material contract, the equipment list and the hourly rates combined with receipts from material suppliers would represent the total cost for the activity. The time allocated by a contractor should be verified by time cards or staff monitoring. The contractor should not pass the material costs through their administrative procedures and add a fee for processing. Consideration should be given for the builder/developer to open an account with material suppliers (i.e., pipe suppliers, concrete companies, etc.). A true savings can be achieved by purchasing material directly from the supplier. Managing the material used by a contractor will result in cost savings.

Lump Sum not to Exceed

The land development bid process is developed to manage a "lump sum not to exceed" contract. If properly followed, this type of contract can provide the highest degree of knowledge of the project costs. A potential problem with a lump sum contract is in the complexity of earthwork operations. Unsuitable soil or rock encountered during construction and not identified in the soil investigation work will cause a problem with the contractor. During the negotiation process, address this problem as an extra work provision in the contract. The lump sum not to exceed contract is extremely beneficial to the developer in controlling costs, knowing costs, and managing costs for the project. The profit margins expected by the developer can be achieved as anticipated in the project pro forma with the lump sum contract. There will always be extenuating circumstances in the field that cause a lump sum not to exceed contract to become a debate between the developer and contractor for payment of extra work. This can be overcome by including the equipment list and the hourly rates with the lump sum contract. The contract provisions should be specific in terms of extra work activities. As long as the extra work is approved by the developer, the contractor can proceed with the work without delay by using the equipment hourly rates and operators to fulfill their work obligations.

For budget ramifications, extras can be handled several ways. A contingency budget item can be included in the overall project pro forma, which has its own separate account. Or each individual land development activity can be budgeted with its own contingency line item. Each of these accounting approaches works. The total land development cost, known or projected with accuracy, is a must before the release of houses or lots for sale.

Once houses or lots are released for sale, the project unknowns, resulting in extras, or the inability to perform the work in an efficient manner will increase the development costs. If these costs are not accounted for in the pro forma, the price of lots or houses will need to be increased. It is extremely important to maintain continuous building operations so that profitable companies can continue to prosper and provide new housing opportunities.

A comprehensive 19-step contract outline, highlighting the provisions of a land development contract, is provided in Figure 12-5. The contract should clearly identify project schedules as being an important element of the work requirements of the contractor. A sample land development contract, as shown in Figure 12-6, has proven to be successful in the implementation of a single-family residential project. Once the contract has been executed, schedule a preconstruction meeting. At the meeting, include the staff, land development contractor, surveyor, utility companies, engineer, governmental officials, and others to discuss the project specifics, mobilization of the land development contractor, and the staging area within the project site. Any last-minute contractual problems can be resolved at that time.

Subsequent regular project meetings are necessary to ensure open communications between the contractor, government inspectors, and developer. Addressing problem areas as they are presented in the field is necessary if the project is to maintain its schedule.

Photo 12-2. Maintaining a Project Schedule. Included in the land development bid process is the requirement that each contractor should submit their construction schedule with each invoice. Contractors will be more inclined to meet their schedules than the schedules imposed by the developer. The key is to have the same goal.

There will be external influences on the project schedule. However, these situations, such as bad weather, cannot be controlled by the owner. As with any project, the schedule should include slack time that accommodates lost days resulting from uncontrollable and unpredictable events. Adverse weather can alter the approach to the schedule, none of which should change the goal of delivering the first housing pad on time.

CONSTRUCTION DOCUMENT REVISIONS

The following list of reasons to change the construction documents can occur in any residential housing project. Changing the construction documents requires the engineering company to assess the change and revise the plans. Revision dates, revision numbers, and reasons for the change should be indicated on the plans. The revised plans should be sent to the appropriate governmental agencies and to the land development contractor for implementation.

Field conditions affecting the project could cause the construction documents to be revised. For example, if a topography bust is discovered and the elevations in the field are not consistent with the design plans, the construction doc-

uments have to be reviewed and, if required, changed to reflect the existing elevations. The land development contractor will benefit from this field problem. Do
not delay the project while negotiating the cost ramifications for correcting a field
problem.

Owner representatives can change the scope of the work or change the construction documents to better reflect a housing design and foundation design consistent with the project goals. The housing product should change as market conditions change. If a developer concludes that the project should be altered to
reflect a different product approach for greater absorption, the developer can
issue a design change notice. For example, preparing pads for slab construction
would alter earthwork quantities if the plans originally called for basement foundations and the negotiated price was based on basements.

Contractors should submit operational design changes through a shop-draw-
ing procedure. If they find a less expensive material or a better way of completing
the work, an approved design change may affect the construction documents. A
change implemented in the field may change the cost of the negotiated agreement
and affect regulatory permits and approvals.

Regulatory or design engineer revisions can affect the design plans. Field
inspections may change the construction documents to reflect an engineering
approach that can accelerate the schedule or reduce costs.

All changes to the construction documents affect the engineer, government
inspections, the developer, the contractor, and houseline contractors. Any change
to the construction documents will affect regulatory permits, approvals, and the
ultimate purchasers of the lots or houses. Any design changes or changes to the
construction documents should be cross referenced to permits and approvals
issued for the project. If no conflicts arise, then the change can be implemented
without delay.

BUDGET VERSUS ACTUAL

Once the project is underway and the contractor is submitting invoices on a
monthly basis, a budget versus actual cost report needs to be distributed on a
monthly basis. A budget versus bid report showing the differences between the
budget and the actual bid proposal is outlined in Figure 12-7. If there are any negative differences between the budget and the bid price, the price of the product
being sold may need to be adjusted to meet profit goals.

CHAPTER 13

Land Development
Project Management

On selection of a land development contractor, the builder/developer must now direct their energies to manage the land development contractor until work is complete. Strive to complete the project on time, within budget constraints, and without field problems. This chapter reviews practical management practices available to oversee field operations.

COMMUNICATION

A daily diary should be maintained by the field superintendent managing the daily activities of the land development contractors. The diary is a historical accounting of the project and should substantiate the actions of the land development contractor. The diary should be specific on matters of compliance with the contract agreement. All land development issues occurring on a daily basis need to be recorded and communicated to all involved parties. The correspondence should be sent to the municipal inspector and to the contractor to ensure that the issues raised can be resolved without delay.

There are several ways to keep track of land development work as it progresses through to completion. The contractor should submit an updated construction schedule with each draw request. Each invoice and schedule should be submitted to the field office—not to the main or corporate office. The draw request and the construction schedule must be reviewed and approved by the personnel responsible for managing that contractor. With each draw request, a simple accounting of the actual costs versus the budget amounts needs to be analyzed before approval of the invoice and submission to the corporate accounting office for payment.

SCHEDULE

Figure 13-1 is an example of a land development progress schedule. This land development master schedule should span the entire infrastructure construction

Photo 13-1. Field Management. Assign field personnel to inspect and approve land development work and invoices for compliance with the contract provisions.

phase. Each activity listed corresponds with the operational requirements of the project. There are certain elements of this schedule that can enhance the management capabilities of the field staff.

The column heading on the schedule provides an illustration of the time span required for each land development activity. At the submission of each draw request, simply indicate the actual work completed during the past payment period. If a land development contractor with sufficient capabilities is hired, it is not uncommon for a residential land development contractor to complete more than $100,000 in land development work in any given month. This level of work will vary from contractor to contractor and site to site, but in land development, money can be expended very rapidly. Thus, with each monthly schedule and invoice, the field staff needs to fully understand the value received from the contractor versus the value requested. Without question, a contractor should not be billing beyond the value received. However, most land development contractors will invoice for the work scheduled to be completed during that payment period. It is common practice to retain 10% of the invoice amount each month.

There are other blocks within the table that show work stoppages, delays, activity completions, and a listing of milestones that are important to review with the progress of the work. As an example, a milestone would be the completion of the first housing pad or the completion of an offsite sewer line so houses could be hooked up to the sewer. For each work activity and each work period, indicate the percentage of work completed on the schedule. This will clearly show where the work is behind schedule or on schedule.

This schedule is an excellent tool for communicating with a financial institution. Also, field personnel can add important general notes to the schedule. This master schedule should be updated on a regular basis and copies distributed to staff.

FIELD OFFICE

The field office should implement another tool of keeping track of work progress. A set of engineering plans should be spliced together showing the complete road layout, lot layout, and water, sewer, and drainage facilities for the project. This overall engineering plan should be tacked to a wall, highly visible to all visitors to the field office. This is especially important for government inspectors, in-house management officers, and outside professionals reviewing and approving construction activities. This plan should show the following:

1. Color code all elements of work that are 100% complete. As an example, color code the water lines as blue for the portion of the water line installed. Red could highlight the sewer line installed within the project. Color coding would represent those elements installed and approved by field personnel.
2. The date the work was completed should be noted next to the color-coded activity on the plans.
3. The initials of the field personnel approving the work should be indicated on the plan next to the date. This field management plan illustrates work completed and clearly shows what is left to be accomplished.
4. Include on this plan the electrical and telephone distribution lines, conduit crossings, and transformer box locations. These facilities should also be color coded to indicate work complete.
5. This plan can also illustrate the work accomplished during a payment period. When an invoice is submitted to the field office, the staff can use the daily diaries and field management plan to understand the extent of the work completed. Work has to be completed to the satisfaction of the company before being color coded on the plan.

All invoices can be accurately and appropriately reviewed for accuracy based on field documentation and recorded in the construction office.

INVOICES AND PAYMENT

A payment schedule form is provided in Figure 13-2. This form should be completed by the contractor. This payment schedule should include the contract amount, any net changes approved, and change orders executed by the contractor and the company. The accounting sheet should show descriptions of work that were negotiated line items within the contract agreement.

SCHEDULE OF VALUES

The schedule of value for each description of work should be included on the payment sheet. The analysis shows previous payments that had been approved, less the work in place. The sum of the two figures would indicate the amount of the work completed. The retainer held is to ensure that warranty issues and quality control of the project are appropriately addressed. The contractor should provide a warranty of the work installed for 1 to 2 years. A sample invoice for the appropriate contract items and amounts is illustrated in Figure 13-3. This form provides a snapshot review of the overall project and can be reviewed and analyzed against the work progress.

RELEASE OF LIEN

A release of lien, as shown in Figure 13-4, should be attached to every payment request submitted by the contractor. Lien laws of individual states should be reviewed so that this portion of the contract can be enforced according to specific state laws. The release of lien is important for the contractor to notify the client that there are no payment problems with any subcontractors or material suppliers. If the release of lien is not submitted, this action could ultimately affect the progress of the project.

PAYMENT

In addition to the release of lien, an additional paragraph within the contract document entitled "payment," as illustrated in the following paragraphs, could further identify the responsibilities of the contractor in accordance with the contract agreement.

1. The contractor shall submit to the company every month—unless otherwise specified in the contract or on demand—a written itemized bill for labor, equipment, and services furnished and materials installed during the preceding month, together with a statement that all indebtedness incurred by the contractor for labor, equipment, materials, and services included in such bill has been paid by the contractor. The company shall have the right to require, as a condition precedent to making any payment hereunder, evidence from the contractor in a form satisfactory to the company that any such indebtedness has been paid and that the contractor has met all of his obligations with regard to the withholding and payment of taxes, social security payments, unemployment compensation contributions, and similar payroll deductions from the wages of employees.

2. The company shall pay such a bill in accordance with the rates, prices, or sums set forth in the various supplements hereto within 2 weeks after approval of the same by the company unless otherwise specified in the contract. The contractor must bill the company for extra work, over and above that for which payment is specified herein within 30 days after the completion of such work. Otherwise he shall be deemed to have waived his right to payment for the same.

3. Notwithstanding the foregoing, it is agreed that any payment by the company of any sums hereunder shall not be deemed to constitute approval or acceptance of the labor, equipment, materials, or services furnished hereunder.

4. Notwithstanding the waiver of mechanics' claims or liens hereinafter referred to, the company shall have the right, before making final payment or payments hereunder, to require the contractor to deliver to the company a general release of liens, in a form satisfactory to the company covering all items of labor, equipment, materials, and services furnished.

5. Anything herein contained to the contrary notwithstanding, the company reserves the right to make payment directly to laborers, material men, subcontractors, sub-subcontractors, or any subcontractors or sub-subcontractors of any of them for or on account of work performed or materials furnished under this agreement. If such payments are made in good faith and on reasonable evidence of their validity, the company shall have no liability in connection therewith and shall deduct such payments from any balance owed to the contractor.

PROGRESS MEETINGS

As each land development project progresses, field personnel should establish regularly scheduled contractors' meetings, including the times, dates, and places. Developers should schedule weekly project meetings on Monday afternoons simply to reanalyze the prior weeks' work and handle any Monday-morning problems that may have arisen over the weekend. Also establish work priorities and issue the new progress schedule for the coming week. These meetings should be held on a weekly basis regardless of the level of work. Prepare a meeting agenda, starting with payment problems, work schedules, regulatory issues, change orders, and an open discussion for the benefit of the field personnel. If held on a regular basis, these meetings should last no more than 1 hour.

FIELD EXTRAS

Time delays are a problem in residential land development projects, and because of delays, additional work may be required of the contractor. Controlling extra fieldwork is critical to the project's financial success. Extras are caused by a difference between the scope of work negotiated versus the actual work required because of changing field conditions. Field extras are either a result of inexperienced personnel reviewing and negotiating a contract or a result of extenuating circumstances not discovered during the field site analysis work.

The ultimate success of a project relies on the contractor to select experienced people to manage and supervise the fieldwork. In the budget process, add a contingency line item for construction extras encountered during construction. The developer should investigate *who* may have caused the problem. There are many reasons for a construction extra, such as:

1. A regulatory requirement imposed by a government engineering inspector
2. A design change that enhances the quality of construction
3. An unknown problem not discovered until under construction
4. A problem with weather conditions
5. A design problem
6. Poor quality of work from subcontractors

After it is determined *what* the problem is, decide on *who* caused the problem. Knowing what the problem is should relate to the contract documents. Determine how the field condition results in a contractual problem. The developer should investigate and determine when the problem occurred. This is accomplished by using the field representative's daily accounting of the work progress, weekly reports or diaries, and the project plan. Discussions with the contractor are important to understand their position on the cause and solution to a problem. Ask why the problem occurred. Land development for residential projects is generally learned through experience, generally bad experience. Minimize field problems during the investigative and design phases of a subdivision project. Land development contractors profit from construction extras. It is the contractor's philosophy that most developers do not investigate the site properly and extensively enough to know all of the site conditions that should be addressed in contract negotiation and are overlooked.

Thus, when the extra work does occur, contractors know their equipment and labor is on the job site, and they are in a better position to negotiate for the work. Some contractors will seek a substantial profit margin for the work to overcome a field problem and to keep the project on schedule. Each problem needs to be assessed by the field staff, engineer, and surveyor. With the contractor, they should be involved in recommending a design solution to a problem. This design, if it is outside the initial scope of work, should then be given to the contractor for a price. For each problem, negotiate a lump sum fee for each scope of work. The lump sum contract agreement becomes an addendum to the contract and describes the work to be done and the price for the work. If the contractor is permitted to proceed without a clear design solution or a negotiated lump sum, the cost of that work will generally be higher, and the contractor's profit margin will far exceed the contingency budgets established at the outset of the project. Construction extras, unfortunately, always seem to surface when production is at its peak and the need to keep on schedule is at its greatest. It is incumbent on all parties to proceed and resolve field conditions in an expedited fashion. A contractor's experience in providing a competitive price, in mobilizing their equipment and material, in handling field problems, and in scheduling work consistent with company goals is an important ingredient of a successful project. The cost of the extras should be analyzed against the budget on a monthly basis. Assessing the ramifications of the cost caused by extras may increase the land development budget and would then require an increase in the sales price of the house or lot. If sales price adjustments need to be made to accommodate the cost extras in land development operations, this decision from the developer must be completed immediately and communicated to the sales staff. If prices need to be increased, a certain date should be established to monitor which homes would be affected by the price increase.

CHANGE ORDER REQUEST

A change order request form, as shown in Figure 13-5, should be filled out by field personnel. It shows the project specifics and the individual who is proposing the change order. This form should be submitted for corporate approval. The actual job site conditions, reasons for the design change, clear justification of the change, and its cost should be sent to the accounting department for assessment of the budget ramifications. There are occasions when the contractor must proceed in correcting a problem without authorization. The remaining portion of the change order form provides for a description of the work to be performed and by which contractor. The change order request is submitted to the field superintendent for his review and approval before proceeding with land development activities.

CHANGE ORDER CONTRACT ADDENDUM

A change order addendum form to the contract is illustrated in Figure 13-6. This is a one-page contract addendum that would indicate the description of the work to be performed. This change order contract forms a part of the base contract agreement so that all of the base contract provisions and requirements are valid.

CHAPTER 14

Land Development Operations

CONSTRUCTION SURVEYING

Residential land development activities are undertaken with field guidance provided by surveying crews. Surveyors provide construction stakeouts for the clearing, excavation, street grades, water and sewer control stakes, electrical and telephone crossings, storm drainage lines, curbs and gutters, and paving operations. The surveying required for housing construction should be a separate contract item. Daily project surveying can be documented by using Figure 14-1.

The land development contractor, in many states, will not accept the responsibility for construction stakeout work. In some states, however, it is general practice in land development work to have the contractor subcontract out for surveying services. Many contractors prefer to subcontract survey control and retain responsibility for the construction stakeout for residential projects. If the contractor accepts the responsibility for surveying, the owner has to manage only one firm. Any land development field problem would be discussed with one company, rather than trying to determine which subcontractor caused the problem. If the contractor does not accept the responsibility for surveying, the owner can negotiate the surveying services fee at a lower amount, thus saving the profit, overhead, and administrative costs the contractor would charge for managing the surveyor.

The surveyor will have their own survey control established in the field. This survey control will be used to set all grade elevations for the infrastructure. If the contractor subcontracts a surveyor, it is advisable to retain a different surveyor to perform the houseline surveying. This would provide a double check of the survey control, elevations, and alignment of the infrastructure. If the same surveying company is used for land development and houseline construction, any discrepancy in the field may not be discovered, and the problem will compound as the construction progresses. If a different houseline surveyor is used, those problems can be discovered, with full disclosure, and corrective measures made. This check-and-balance approach ensures the layout is consistent with the design plans.

CLEARING OPERATIONS

Clearing operations can proceed once the surveyor has marked the clearing limits within the street right-of-way and also on the lots to be cleared for housing construction. Most surveyors mark the clearing limits by using flags or painting a mark on the trees to be saved at the limit of clearing. The clearing subcontractor should be working within those clearing limits and proceed with the stumping and chipping operations in a continuous manner. The clearing operations should not be interrupted for other tasks. A maximum number of lots should be cleared for housing operations to maximize the equipment use onsite.

The land development contract should indicate the methods the contractor will use to remove the stumps from the site. Some contractors will use a stump grinder and mix the grindings with the topsoil. Some contractors will chip a majority of the trees. It is important to locate the chip pile in an area that will not hinder subsequent land development or housing construction activities. In addition to the right-of-way and phase-one lot clearing, the contractor should also clear a few lots beyond the first phase. The additional area would provide a location for the storage of materials, staging of equipment, construction trailers, and administrative trailers onsite. It is advisable to reserve one of the better lots for the field offices.

SELECTIVE CLEARING

The owner's representative should be walking the centerline of the right-of-way and walk each lot located within phase one of construction. If there are significant trees within pad areas or within right-of-way areas that should be saved, this information should be conveyed to the design engineer and to the regulatory agencies. In many cases, the saving of trees located in building pads and right-of-way areas becomes almost impossible. However, there are several ways to save specimen trees if the species and size of the tree warrant such an action by improved grading operations, tree wells, and underdrains.

Trees that should be saved could be transplanted to buffer areas or to staging areas for future use. Tree spades come in various sizes to handle significantly sized trees. The marketing potential of saving mature trees within a subdivision cannot be overemphasized, especially when new vegetation purchased from a wholesale landscaper cannot match the maturity of transplanted trees. Many tree-spade operations can be paid for from the savings resulting from the transplanting operations. A mature street scene is instantaneous and has great market appeal. The value of saving site trees is tremendous because new homebuyers want not only a new home but a mature street scene.

EARTHWORK OPERATIONS

Once the site and lots have been cleared, earthwork operations will commence. It is advisable to have a surveyor, soil scientist, and engineer become involved in daily earthwork operations. They become the owners' third-party inspectors on the job site. Figures 14-2 and 14-3 can be used for reporting daily and weekly construction activities. Once the topsoil is stripped from the lots and rights-of-way, it is stockpiled in a cleared area selected by the owner. The right-of-way topsoil is generally stockpiled in an area where it can be accessed by pans or loaders and trucks. The topsoil being stripped from each individual lot is generally stockpiled on the higher portion of the lot to facilitate drainage. Once the topsoil is removed, soil scientists can assess the type of material that exists on the lot. If there is unsuitable material located underneath the housing foundation area, a soil scientist will determine the extent of the work required to ensure structural integrity of the foundation. The soil scientist should sign and seal their soils investigation work and inspect the contractor's excavation and removal of all unsuitable material.

Mass filling, cutting, and rough grading of each site is undertaken with a schedule that should be met without undue delay. Weather will have an effect on earthwork operations and the project schedule. Most delays can be managed properly and the schedule maintained with the cooperation of the contractor, together with experienced and knowledgeable operators. The contractor should not deviate from the design plans unless there is an approved change order. The land development contractor will succeed financially if the operators handle the material just one time. If the developer can show the contractor how he will make money on the job site, the contractor will approach the project in a positive manner. This will result in profits for the developer and the contractor.

HOUSELINE LAND DEVELOPMENT

The surveyor locates the house foundation by setting four corner foundation survey stakes with 15-ft offsets and then indicates the cut-or-fill requirements for the pad construction. If there is a cut for the foundation, the fill material generated should be used on that specific lot, if possible. Therefore, the earthwork calculations should take into account the fill generated from foundations, driveways, and other flat work on each particular housing lot. The pad should be built 10 feet beyond the perimeter of the house foundation for ease of houseline construction and accessibility to the construction of the home. The clearing limits around each home should be a minimum of 15 feet around the house. After the pad is completed and before the start of foundation work, a soils consultant should take soil compaction tests on the building pad. The soil consultant should certify the pad is in compliance with the applicable building codes. The rough grading of lots should also be completed with the use of surveying grade stakes. The residential land development contractor should hire equipment operators experienced in housing projects. The contractor should compact the building pads with rollers to achieve compaction that complies with building code requirements. The soils consultant should also inspect all fill areas to ensure that the operation is in compliance with lift requirements and compaction standards. Once the fill areas have been inspected, tested, and approved by the appropriate regulatory agencies, backfilling within roadway sections and foundations is permitted.

On the completion of the final grading, a landscape subcontractor moves the stockpiled topsoil and spreads it on the lot and the right-of-way area. This area would be seeded or sodded to complete the lot preparation. The houseline superintendents must have the outside houseline work, driveways, patios, sidewalks, etc., completed before the final grading and seeding take place. The landscape subcontractor will use the wood chips generated from the clearing operations in the tree-save areas, which will reduce the need for additional seeded areas. Residential lots left in a more natural condition will be more appealing and marketable to a majority of buyers.

The balancing of cut-and-fill earthwork operations is essential to the success of the project. Any soil material imported to the project site should be certified for its use as structural material in roadways or foundation areas.

If there are substantial numbers of trees and stumps, the grubbing operations will leave significant voids in the project site. These areas may require additional fill over and above what may have been calculated by the engineer. Thus, during the budget process, the fill quantities should be increased by 15% to accommodate this type of clearing operations and for the compaction of the material. This percent increase is normally determined by the soils consultant and is based on the site soil conditions.

EROSION AND SEDIMENTATION CONTROL

Before earthwork operations start, soil erosion and sedimentation control measures need to be implemented in the field. This activity generally includes a stone tracking pad at the access point onto existing roadways. This stone pad is designed to remove any mud, dirt, or debris from the trucks, machinery, or equipment leaving or entering the project site. Installation of a silt fence is another soil conservation measure. The silt fence is installed to protect adjoining properties or wetland areas from sedimentation.

The land development contractor should install inlet protection over the inlet grates as needed. Inlet protection will filter stormwater before it enters the inlets and is ultimately released from the project site. This can be accomplished cost effectively by using a mat with stone over the inlet grates or by using hay bales. The contractor should maintain these protective measures to ensure compliance

Photo 14-1. Erosion and Sedimentation Control. The stormwater management facility should be designed to control erosion and sedimentation during construction. Proper design will minimize upfront costs and maximize the use of the facility.

with Soil Conservation District requirements. For earthwork operations, the contractor should be required, by contract, to provide street cleaning on a continuous basis to eliminate sedimentation entering the storm drainage system, to control dust during dry periods, and to ensure the job site has an acceptable appearance for any prospective homebuyers.

UTILITY INSTALLATIONS

The soils engineer should use the soils testing information to determine the seasonal high water table and the necessity for well pointing during underground utility installation. Dewatering is an expensive operation and needs to be addressed in the contract before commencement of the work.

Conflicts between the sewer line and other utilities are found at crossings and when parallel lines are less than 10 feet apart. Review with the contractor all potential conflict areas illustrated on the plans. Make sure the utility crossings, horizontally and/or vertically, are not in conflict before construction. Many sewer and drainage lines are set at slopes governed by outlet elevations, and the locations are difficult to change in the field. Waterline elevations and locations are much easier to change in the field if a conflict occurs.

ELECTRIC, TELEPHONE, CABLE

The electric, telephone, gas, and cable utility companies use their own crews or subcontractors for installations. The difference in company crews versus subcontractors can entail a substantial difference in time, quality, and effort in residential community installations. Utility companies are often unilateral in their design approach to a project. Their plans are specific enough to find any conflicts that may occur in the field as a result of their design plans.

Conflicts in street lights, transformers, and pedestal locations should be checked against the plot plans for each lot. The service locations from a transformer to a lot should dictate the right- or left-hand garage type. If it is customary to install the electrical panel in the garage, the garage should be located on the side of the electrical service and as per the electrical layout design. Otherwise an additional charge could be assessed against the lot for additional service length for the house.

Most conflicts caused by electric, telephone, and cable companies pertain to the location of their pedestals or transformers within the right-of-way area. Their equipment locations could affect drainage swales, driveways, sidewalks, street trees, grade elevations, etc.

WATER AND SEWER

Once utility services are installed, many water and sewer companies require an underground utility contractor to etch a "W" or "S" into the curb face so the lateral can be located once the project has been completed. Field representatives or the project surveyor should field-locate the valve boxes, clean-outs, and fire hydrants and note them on the project map for future reference. Planners will suggest that clean-outs and valve boxes should be located outside of a driveway. This may have been accommodated in the design, but the implementation in the field must be managed properly.

To expedite the utility company's installation of their facilities, contract separately with the land development contractor for the installation of utility conduit for road crossings. Include the cost of conduit road crossings in the budget. This expenditure will help keep the project on schedule because the project does not have to wait for the utility company. The utility companies, as long as the conduit meets their specifications and is in accordance with their regulations, can then install their lines according to their schedule. This is not a problem as long as the first home has service when needed.

STORM DRAINAGE

Drainage installations should start with the stormwater management facility so it can also function as the soil and erosion sedimentation facility. Seed the

Photo 14-2. Land Development Operations. The quality and longevity of a roadway begins with a structurally sound and properly graded road base. This approach is also true for sidewalks, curbs, utilities, and building pads for foundations.

stormwater basin immediately after it is final graded. This will minimize the future maintenance requirements of the facility. Some municipalities require the fencing of stormwater management ponds and access gates and roads for maintenance purposes. Choose the proper fencing material if it is critical to the overall appearance of the project. Depending on the location of the stormwater management pond, a typical chain-link fence may be appropriate. However, if the facility is located in and among housing units, a black or green vinyl chain-link fence would be a better choice because the color would blend into the background. This type of fencing and evergreen landscaping would transform the basin into a positive attribute of the project.

CURB AND GUTTER INSTALLATIONS

The surveyor provides a field alignment and grade stakes for curb installation. If the project is preplanned with right- or left-hand garage and driveway locations, the surveyor should mark in the field where the driveway is located. Thus, the curb subcontractor would install depressed curbs, driveway aprons, and sidewalks consistent with the overall plan of the project. The soils engineer should randomly take compaction tests under the curb sections to ensure the sub-base has sufficient structural integrity to support the curb without deflection or failure. The cost of curb replacement and concrete removal can be substantial.

Communicate with the surveyor which lots can be designated with a one- or two-car driveway, so the correct width of the curb cut can be installed in the field. To facilitate houseline construction, include in the land development agreement that the contractor needs to include *maintain access provisions* to each house. Also, a provision needs to be included concerning the protection of the curb from damage caused by large equipment or heavy supply trucks. The infrastructure is extremely vulnerable to damage from suppliers of heavy housing construction materials, such as concrete, lumber, and drywall. Damage to concrete curbs by chipping, cracking, or causing settlement through the lack of protection will double the cost of curb installation.

Each individual lot needs to be rough graded to ensure access for houseline subcontractors, material suppliers, well drilling equipment, and landscapers. If proper care is taken and the subcontractors are notified of areas that can be used for access, the potential for damaging the infrastructure is minimized. Proper precautions taken during construction will eliminate conflict or arbitration as a result of infrastructure failure. If proper precautions are not taken, the cause of the infrastructure failure needs to be determined and actions taken to eliminate the cause.

PAVEMENT

The final pavement should be installed when 90% to 95% of the homes have been closed or are beyond the sheetrock stage. Install street trees on the lot before closing the house. This will eliminate the need for any subsequent landscaping on the lot after it is closed. This will also facilitate an approval for maintenance bond status.

Once the final paving is completed, request the surveyor to prepare an as-built plan from right-of-way line to right-of-way line. This as-built plan, along with the completion of government punch lists, will expedite the process of having the project released to a maintenance bond status. Take pavement depth measurements during the inspection of pavement construction. Use the roadway construction report, as shown in Figure 14-4, to record the inspection observations. This will also facilitate the acceptance of the right-of-way by a municipality or an HOA.

LAND DEVELOPMENT PUNCH LISTS

Completing infrastructure punch list items is a time-consuming, difficult, and costly aspect of land development. Most punch lists are items the contractors on the project can complete with all due diligence. However, if the punch list lingers and is not completed, this will provide an opportunity for additional punch list items to be added at a future date. Once the subcontractors leave the job site, it is more difficult to get them back to repair any problems listed on the punch list. It is better to get the job done by completing the punch list without delay so the performance bond can be released. The longer the delay, the more difficult it is to achieve maintenance bond status.

Any street traffic control devices, stop signs, street signs, yield signs, etc., should be installed in accordance with traffic control standards. If necessary, install speed limit signs for the subdivision. If the residential street design is appropriate, speed limit signs would not be needed because the road alignment, horizontally and vertically, would control vehicle speed within the subdivision.

Land development field operations must be properly managed to ensure that quality construction is maintained at its highest level. A strong field management team will result in adherence to a project schedule and enforcement of budget constraints.

CHAPTER 15

Land Development as a Business

In the land development business, there are many people associated with designing, permitting, and approving subdivision projects. Very few of these people enjoy the challenges of taking raw land to finished lots. This chapter is an overview of the relationships between these special interest groups and their influence on the land development process.

The influence these special interest groups have on the success of a land development project is extraordinary. The external pressures brought on by the various groups have a direct bearing on a land development company's ability to earn a profit. The following vested interest groups not only directly affect a company's ability to operate as an ongoing concern but directly affect the ability of a buyer to own a home.

GOVERNMENT

Local government controls the growth patterns of its community. Regional, state, and federal governments are structured to oversee projects and to ensure compliance with their regulations, standards, and criteria. Local government's attitude toward housing varies widely across the country and even from street to street. Practical and progressive local governments generally are advocates of new housing projects. Their positive actions result in communities being developed in a way that benefits those who live and work in their community.

Those communities that control growth through governmental restrictions subject themselves to unpredictable economic growth. Restrictive growth control or excessive development regulations adversely affect only people living in that community. Growth controls are instituted by government by down zoning property. This action reduces the number of housing units allowed per acre and therefore reduces the supply of buildable land in the community. The law of supply and demand, or the lack of, will ultimately increase the cost of housing. In addition, raw land very rarely loses value unless that value is affected by government action. The responsibility of existing community infrastructure improvements is now being passed on to the developers of new housing projects. Reducing the availability of land, increasing the cost of development, and inflating the value of land affect the ability of future generations to own a home.

A balanced community encourages business and industrial expansion and prepares for legitimate and practical housing growth. Local government should balance the economic stability of the community for the betterment of society. The strong traditions of living and working in a community, for the community, must change government's grip on housing for housing to succeed as a basic industry of the country.

BUSINESS

The business community is active in the Chamber of Commerce and various civic organizations but rarely publicly supports new housing projects. The business community should become more involved in the growth pattern of a community. The business community will benefit from an active progrowth government. The business leadership should encourage progrowth political agendas for housing to become a part of the business community

CITIZENS

All too often, the populace participates at public hearings by presenting only negative points of view against housing projects. Very rarely will anyone who is in favor of a project attend a planning board meeting. It is all too common for the citizens to use key emotional issues to persuade planning board members and politicians to reject housing projects.

There is a definite no-growth attitude in many communities. Citizens use the "problems" of traffic, water, waste water, environment, safety, security, etc., against housing projects. A sincere and concerted effort to overcome the public no-growth attitude may be too difficult to ask, or even achieve. Thus, the citizen motto of "Not in my back yard!" has to be debated by continuing to ask the question of "Where will my children live?"

ENVIRONMENT

Environmental regulations are the most emotional and restrictive regulatory approaches affecting housing developments today and for many years to come. Environmental issues of endangered species, endangered plants, wetland protection, flood plains, coastal areas, and open-space protection have the greatest effect on housing affordability. Environmental regulations will become only more restrictive and managed by the regulatory sector. Builder/developers must learn

Photo 15-1. Residential Infrastructure. Subdivision improvements are taken for granted only until they fail to function properly. If designed and constructed correctly, the infrastructure will function without fanfare while becoming an integral part of the landscape.

how to work within the environmental community and the regulations imposed at the local, state, or federal levels. Housing development is a positive environmental contribution to society. The builder whose business becomes environmentally "green" will be consistent with the demands of the future homeowner.

LEGAL

The legal structure involved in housing has become an unbelievable bureaucratic web that entangles housing progress. Legal representation of special interest groups affects the way a project is built and homes are sold. The liabilities facing building companies have overshadowed the enthusiasm of building a home. Builder/developers should seek to negotiate resolution of problems and keep all conflict issues out of the legal arena. This will save money, time, and effort while channeling all energy into building subdivisions on time and within budget. A negotiated settlement of a problem remains the best solution to a legal situation.

POLITICAL

The political community moves with the tide of public opinion. Successful developers design projects by conforming with all government regulations, reducing the number of variances, and eliminating design waivers. Any project in compliance with the master plan, zoning regulations, subdivision ordinances, and technical standards should be approved regardless of local opposition or political attitudes. Builder/developers will increase their chances of success at the planning board by providing quality living environments for future homebuyers.

HOMEOWNER ASSOCIATIONS

Once a project is turned over to an HOA, homeowner interests are protected by this central organization, which is formed with financial stability. Many HOAs become adversarial with the developer and will politically affect future projects.

HOAs tend to seek builder remedies for issues governed by local ordinances. In many single-family subdivisions, HOAs are created to own and maintain stormwater facilities because the municipality will not accept the responsibility. Because HOAs are overextending their powers, many builders are including common areas in individual lots to eliminate the need for an HOA.

PROFITS

The profit margin of a development company continues to be restricted by regulations. Land price, value, and cost will determine the profit margins achieved on any one particular project. The housing style, products, and project attributes will increase or decrease the absorption and affect the cashflow needs of a company. However, it is the land price and value that will ultimately determine the profitability of the company.

REPUTATION AND CORPORATE IMAGE

Builder/developers must continue to improve their public image through success. Reputation is supported by achieving quality construction, meeting public commitments, addressing warranty issues, and providing service to the customer. A sense of cooperation with government will reinforce the company's reputation within the community. A highly successful marketing campaign is the testimonial of previous buyers because referrals are the basic foundation for housing sales. An impeccable reputation built by satisfied customers reflects a corporate image of professionalism and leadership within the industry.

EFFECT ON SOCIETY

Every industry has a sector that is self-centered. Their lack of sensitivity to the homebuying public unfairly represents the building community as a whole. A sincere distrust of the building community, coupled with builders taking advantage of the public, is a very difficult roadblock to overcome. There are few accolades

Photo 15-2. Quality Improvements. The quality of land development activities changes as design standards change. The level of quality acceptable to the government will govern the cost to develop land. The cost of residential improvements has no relationship with the marketplace or the market's ability to pay for the quality.

for the building community, regardless of the positive effect housing has on society. It is a silent reward for the building community to know that their project provides affordable, safe, and efficient housing for all people.

DESIGN PROFESSIONALS

Design firms actively involved in the building industry must uphold the ideals of the builder/developer. A quality living environment is the greatest achievement of any technical designer. With all of the troubles and complexities of the building industry, the completion of a well-conceived project overshadows the history of problems and issues confronted by each project.

LAND DEVELOPMENT INDUSTRY CHANGES

Projecting how the land development industry will change in the future is difficult. Each project is influenced by a number of people and by excessive regulations imposed at many levels of government. The land development industry will be very slow to change because changes in housing must be well received by all vested interest groups before change is realized.

Large regional builder/developers will not be able to consistently compete at the local level. Builders of 10 to 20 homes per year will continue to dominate fringe markets. Developing land for use by builders is not an easy business. The need for business segmentation is not a result of regulations but an evolvement from regulation.

If new to this industry, welcome aboard! The complexities, challenges, and efforts are all worthwhile when a quality subdivision can be constructed and houses built for families who need a home. By implementing the techniques outlined in this textbook, the housing professional can build and sustain a quality of life that should be cherished by all.

Appendix

COMPETITIVE HOUSING MARKET PROFILE

The housing research development status report, market profile, and design features report will clearly define the market and assist in making the decisions on what to build and sell. Company goals will dictate the market segment needed to complement the housing project inventory of the company. The selection of a starter market with fast absorption or a custom home market with a slow unpredictable absorption may result in the same profitablity over time.

HOUSING RESEARCH DEVELOPMENT STATUS REPORT

This report will identify which projects will have product and will indicate the level of inventory within the marketplace. Use this information to judge the market segmentation of the product line.

A. **Development status report** will describe:
1. Number of planned units in each project
2. Units completed - sold or unsold
3. Units under construction - sold or unsold
4. Units completed - sold or unsold
5. Units remaining available for sale

B. **Product design features report** will describe:
1. Master Bedroom
   a. Size
   b. Location
   c. Separate dressing room
   d. Separate sitting room
   e. Ceiling features, such as, volume, tray, etc.
   f. Walk-in closets
   g. Fireplace
   h. Flooring
   i. Other
2. Master bedroom bath
   a. Separate tub and shower
   b. Whirlpool tub
   c. Double vanity
   d. Vanity top material
   e. Manufacturer of faucets
   f. Enclosed water closet area
   g. Flooring
   h. Other

Figure 1-2. Competitive Housing Market Profile.

3. Kitchen
    a. Style
    b. Counter island
    c. Separate pantry
    d. Separate breakfast nook
    e. Eat-in kitchen
    f. Access to garage
    g. Access to laundry room
    h. Appliances offered as standard
        1) Refrigerator
        2) Dishwasher
        3) Garbage disposal
        4) Oven
        5) Range
        6) Microwave oven
        7) Number of sinks
        8) Other
    i. Cabinets
        1) Style
        2) Material
    j. Counter tops
        1) Style
        2) Material
    k. Flooring
    l. Other
4. Exterior
    a. Finish (i.e., vinyl, wood, stucco, etc.)
    b. Veneer (i.e., stone, brick, etc.)
    c. Roof shingle
    d. Windows
    e. Garage doors
    f. Shutters
    g. Other
5. Interior
    a. Number of bedrooms
    b. Number of baths
    c. Covered porch
    d. Center hall foyer, clear story
    e. Formal foyer
    f. Air conditioning
    g. Ceiling heights
    h. Fireplace
    i. Flooring
    j. Security system
    k. Number of car garages
    l. Basement
    m. Patio or deck
    n. Other

Figure 1-2. Competitive Housing Market Profile—*continued.*

SITE EVALUATION FACTORS

Factor to Be Evaluated	General Source of Information
Boundary survey and acreage	Deed, tax maps, previous surveys, tax offices, restrictions running with the land such as easements
Zoning: lot, building restrictions	Zoning maps, local zoning board, building department
Site improvements and planning policies	Local planning department, subdivision regulations, county planning office
Topography	United States Geological Survey 7.5ft quadrangle maps, local planning department, field surveys, aerial maps, local land owners, library
Soils	Soil survey prepared by the United States Department of Agriculture Soil Conservation Service, on-site subsurface exploratory borings or test pits, contact septic installers and contractors
Floodplain and drainage	Reports prepared by the United States Army Corps of Engineers, state or local department of environmental protection, FEMA, engineering and road departments: public works departments
Water system	Local water authority or water company, fire marshall
Water from wells	State geological survey, state health department, local approving authority, well drillers
Sanitary sewer system	Local sewer authority, state water control board, engineering departments

Figure 1-3. Site Evaluation Factors.

Factor to Be Evaluated	General Source of Information
On-site sanitary system	State health department, local approving authority, septic installers
Freshwater wetlands	State wetlands mapping, local planning offices, field survey
Adjacent or nearby subdivision plans	Local planning and engineering offices
Roads, traffic, and access Future road improvement plans	Local planning departments, state department of transportation, engineering departments
Hydrology/geology, aquifer recharge	State geological survey, local planning department, contact well drillers
Vegetative cover	Site inspection, aerial photographs
Gas and electric	Local power company, state public utility commission
Telephone	Local telephone company, state public utility commission
Archeological/historical significance	State historical society, library
Storm-water management	Local county engineer or department of public works, local planning office, state or regional agencies
Sediment and erosion control	Local department of public works, soil conservation service
Parks/recreation	Local or state parks planning office or recreation board
Schools	Board of education
Landscaping	Local planning department, local nurseries, library, landscape contractors
Transportation availability	Bus, rail, airports for commuting
Public services	Police, fire emergency, trash pick-up
Shopping	Malls, strip centers, local chamber of commerce

Figure 1-3. Site Evaluation Factors—*continued.*

LAND EVALUATION SCOREBOOK

Parcel Lot and Block_____ **Date**_____

Location_____

Factor	Assigned Point Totals				Score
	1	2	3	4	
Distance to Major Population Centers	30mi	20 mi	10 mi	5 mi	_____
Distance to Interstate Highway	10 mi	5 mi	3 mi	2 mi	_____
Distance to Nearest Shopping	5 mi	4 mi	3 mi	2 mi	_____
Distance to Nearest School	5 mi	4 mi	3 mi	2 mi	_____
Distance to Nearest Public Services	5 mi	4 mi	3 mi	2 mi	_____
Distance to Nearest Competition	5 mi	4 mi	3 mi	2 mi	_____
Condition of Road Frontage	Poor	Fair	Good	Excellent	_____
Topography	Low	Flat	Rolling	Hilly	_____
Extent of Slopes Over 10 %	75–85	50–75	25–50	Under 25%	_____
Woods	Poor	Fair	Good	Excellent	_____
Soil	Poor	Fair	Good	Excellent	_____
Rock	Extensive	Frequent	Occasional	None	_____
Natural Gas	3 mi	2 mi	1 mi	At site	_____

Figure 1-4. Land Evaluation Scorebook.

Factor	Assigned Point Totals				Score
	1	2	3	4	
Electric Power	3 mi	2 mi	1 mi	At site	_____
Public Water Supply	None	500–1,000 ft	100–500 ft	Within 100 ft	_____
Public Sewers	None	500–1,000 ft	100–500 ft	Within 100 ft	_____
Wetlands Portion of Site	Extensive	20%	10%	Under 5%	_____
Approximate % of Land Available for Lots	Under 25%	50%	75%	100%	_____
Single-Family Zoning	1 acre	1 acre	½ acre	¼ acre	_____
Subdivision Standards	Excessive	Average	Limited	None	_____
General Impression of Site for Single-Family Homes	Poor	Not First Choice	Further Investigate	Great	_____

General Comments: _____
_____
_____
_____

Rating of Site_____

Prepared By/Date _____

A site with a rating of over 55 should be further evaluated for development.

1 ft = 30 cm; 1 mi = 1.6 km; 1 acre = 0.4 ha

Figure 1-4. Land Evaluation Scorebook—*continued*.

SITE ANALYSIS CHECKLIST

REPORT BY:_____**DATE:**_____
LOT:_____**BLOCK:**_____**LOCATION:**_____

1. Highlight special land characteristics that would cause a "NO" purchase decision and indicate any cost implications.

a. Poor soil	j. Poor surface drainage
b. Topography	k Flood hazard
c. Heavy Vehicular traffic	l. High water table
d. Heavy air traffic	m.Unsightly views
e. Vegetation	n. Demolition requirements
f. Noise problems	o. Environmental problems
g. Odor problems	p. Illegal dumping on-site
h. Wetlands	q. Railroad tracks nearby
i. Condition of adjacent property	r. Interstate highways nearby

 Other:_____
2. List Soil Classification
   a. Advantages
   b. Disadvantages
   c. Depth to seasonal high water table
   d. Summary of soils report for the site

   _____ --

   _____

   e. Will soil conditions cause excessive development or building costs?
   _____

3. Topography
   a. Source of the topography survey
   b. Date of aerial topography flight taken:_____
   c. Topography map checked by a field survey? Date:_____
   d. Will heavy vegetation or steep slopes effect the topo accuracy?
   e. Examine USGS map and list any discrepancies in the topo_____
   _____

4. Buildable area
   a. What percentage of the property is
      low___flat___rolling___hilly___
   b. Indicate on the survey any areas to be excluded as buildable area.
   c. Are there any cost implications as a result of the topography?
5. Boundary Survey
   a. Are the exact boundary lines known and verified
   b. Are there any property line discrepancies such as overlaps, etc.
   c. Is the seller responsible for resolving title problems
   d. Boundary survey is available by date:_____
   e. Summary of discussions with the surveyor of the property
   _____
   f. If the property has not been surveyed, will the seller pay for the work?
   g.Surveys available for the adjacent properties_____
      What are the impacts of the adjacent property on the site?_____

Figure 1-5. Site Analysis Checklist.

What are the cost implications?_____

6. Does the land have enough natural fall for drainage purposes?
   a. What is the effect of the topo on earthwork operations?
   b. Is there drainage off-site that drains onto this site?
   c. What are the cost implications?
7. What % of the property might be considered nonbuildable due to:
   topography_____woods_____soil_____
   rock_____wetlands_____easements_____
   What is the net buildable area to be used for residential development?_____

Based upon the density factor of the zone, calculate the number of lots based upon the net buildable area_____

8. Vegetation growth is: Light___Moderate___Heavy____
   Are there tree-save programs required for this site?
   Cost implications for clearing operations or tree-save programs.
9. Any natural or man-made features on site: streams___lakes___ponds____
   rivers_____storm-water management facilities___flood zone____
   Should any of these features be used as a site amenity?_____
   What are the cost implications for making the above features into site
   amenities?_____
10. Does the property have road frontage in _____ft.
    Public or private road access?_____
    Existing right-of-way width of frontage road_____
    Dedication of right-of-way required along the property frontage in____ft.
    What is the road surface of the frontage road?_____
    Frontage road is owned by: Federal___State___County___City___
                          Private_____Other___
    If private, what are the ingress/egress rights assigned to the site?

    _____
    List future improvement plans of the off-site roads near the site:

    _____
    What are the cost implications to acquire right-of-way access for ingress
    and egress or for road improvements:_____
11. Natural Gas Facilities
        Distance to line
        Capacity required to serve subdivision
        New line required
        Cost implications
12. Electric Lines
        Distance to nearest lines
        Relocation of poles required
        Cost implications
13. Water Lines
        Distance to nearest line
        Sufficient capacity to serve the subdivision
        New line required
        Need to loop the water lines for the system

Figure 1-5. Site Analysis Checklist—*continued.*

Sufficient pressure to serve the property (check with the Fire Department)
Cost implications
14. Private Wells
Depth_____Quantity Expected_____
Quality of the water_____
Treatment required_____restrictions on use - irrigation_____cost_____
15. Sewer Lines
Distance to nearest line
Sufficient line capacity to serve the property
Sufficient treatment plant capacity to serve the project
Alternative sewer systems available, such as septic systems
Cost implications
16. Other Utilities
Telephone Company Prewiring cost_____
Cable TV Company Prewiring cost_____
Street Lights required Cost:_____
17. Storm Drainge System
Distance to the nearest storm drain
Sufficient size to handle flow from the site
Cost implications
18. List the nature of the adjacent properties:
North:_____
East:_____
West:_____
South:_____
19. Contact List
Planner:_____Phone#_____
Comments_____
Engineer:_____Phone#_____
Comments_____
Soils Engineer:_____Phone#_____
Comments_____
Architect:_____Phone#_____
Comments_____
Environmentalist:_____Phone#_____
Comments_____
Traffic Engineer:_____Phone#_____
Comments_____
Surveyor:_____Phone#_____
Comments_____

20. Site analysis conclusions and recommendations:
_____
_____
_____
_____
_____

Figure 1-5. Site Analysis Checklist—*continued.*

TYPICAL RESIDENTIAL APPROVAL PROCESS

A. LAND————————————————————————————————————**B.CONCEPT LAND PLAN**

Marketability
Regulatory Analysis
Site Analysis
Value Analysis

Engineering
Soils
Environmental
Traffic
Architecture
Landscape Architecture
Land Planning

C. FINAL and PRELIMINARY IMPROVEMENT PLANS
  Army Corps of Engineers
    Dredge and Fill
    Wetlands
  State Environmental Department
    Wetlands
    Flood Plains
    Impact Statements
    Well Permits
  Sewer Authority
    Local
    Regional
    State
  Water Authority
    Local
    Regional
    State
  Municipal
    Planning Board
    Shade-Tree Commission
    Environmental Commission
    Fire Department
    Health Department
    Tax Office
  County Planning Board
  Soil Conservation District
  State Department of Transportation

1. Post Performance Bonds and Inspection Fees

2. Start Land Development and Obtain Signatures on Final Plat

3. Record Final Plat and Apply for Building Permits

4. Construct Building Pads; Building Permits Issued

5. Land Development 70% Complete; Reduce Bond and Close First House

6. Close Last House; Turnover Infrastructure; Obtain Maintenance Bond

Figure 1-6. Typical Residential Approval Process.

COMPREHENSIVE REGULATORY CHECKLIST

Report By:_____ Date:_____

Lot:_____Block:_____Location:_____

1. Municipal planning board address:_____
   Planning board secretary:_____Phone#:_____
   Fax#:_____
2. Municipal engineer address:_____
   Engineer contact:_____Phone#:_____
   Fax#:_____
3. Police department contact:_____Phone#:_____
   Fire Department contact:_____Phone#:_____
   Emergency Services Contact:_____Phone #:_____

4. What is the local attitude toward residential development:_____
   Planning board members:_____
   Neighbors:_____

5. Municipal architectural review board contact:_____Phone#:_____

6. Obtain all relevant ordinances and indicate cost problems with regulations:
   Subdivision:_____
   Building:_____
   Zoning:_____
   Development:_____
   Water:_____
   Sewer:_____
   Master plan:_____
   Growth management plan:_____

7. Present zoning of the site:_____
   Density permitted:_____
   Minimum lot dimensions: Size_____Width_____Depth_____
   Lot frontage:_____Minimum Sq Ft of building:_____
   Setbacks: Front_____Sides_____Rear_____

8. Does the local municipality require subdivision bonds?_____
   Accept? Letter of Credits_____Performance Bond_____Lenders Agreement_____
   Cash Requirements_____Bond Amount Calculation_____
   Will partial bond releases be approved?_____
   Maintenance Bonds Required?_____Number of Years?_____
   Manitenance Bond amount calculation_____

9. Property in Special Regulatory Zone: Forest____Wildlife___Fire Hazard____Fault___
   Historical___Flood___Dump____Acquifer___
   Archeological____Environmentally Sensitive____

Figure 1-7. Comprehensive Regulatory Checklist.

10. List Governmental Policies on impact fees, such as schools, parks, recreation, sewers, etc.

_____

_____

11. List unusual subdivision requirements and potential cost implications:

_____

_____

12. List basic steps in subdivision approval process including time table:

_____

_____

_____

13. Indicate political climate toward housing projects:

_____

_____

14. Summarize discussions with
    Planning department:_____

_____

_____

    Engineering department:_____

_____

    Building department:_____

_____

_____

    Zoning department:_____

_____

_____

    Planning board member:_____

_____

_____

15. Summarize regulatory assessment of proposed site and subdivision goals (pros and cons)

_____

_____

_____

_____

Figure 1-7. Comprehensive Regulatory Checklist—*continued.*

VALUE ANALYSIS CHECKLIST

Report By:_____Date:_____

Lot:_____Block:_____Location:_____

1. Comparison of price per acre or price per lot with other sites under consideration:
   Higher (Why):_____
   _____
   Lower (Why):_____
   _____

2. What is the potential use for this land?_____

3. When would this land be ready to close lots/homes?_____0–1yr____1–2yrs____3–4 yrs

4. Is the price of the land low for the land to appreciate from inflation or speculation?____

5. What did simalar property sell for: 1 yr ago_____3 yrs ago_____5 yrs ago_____

6. What are the land price trends for the area in the future?_____

7. How long can this land be held in inventory while approvals are obtained?_____

8. What is the raw land per lot objective for this site?_____

9. Will the price objectives be met once the project obtains all regulatory permits and
   approvals?_____

10. Why buy this site? Investment_____Design, Approve and Sell_____Build Out_____

11. Will this property be used for our own purposes?_____

12. Outstanding reasons for buying this land:_____
    _____
    _____
    _____

13. Outstanding reasons for not buying this land:_____
    _____
    _____

14. **PROCEED**_____**REJECT**_____

Figure 1-8. Value Analysis Checklist.

LAND PURCHASE CHECKLIST

Report By:_____Date:_____

Lot:_____Block:_____Location:_____

1. Size of parcel_____ac. Zoning_____Lot size_____

   Number of lots based on zoning requirements and gross acres_____

2. What portion of the site has been excluded in computing net buildable area_____

   Net buildable area:_____

   Number of lots based on net buildable area:_____

3. Any unusual cost considerations: On-site_____

                                    Off-site_____

4. Present offer based on: Acreage_____

                          Net buildable area_____

                          Number of net lot yield_____

                          Comparable land values_____

5. **Asking Price**_____**Offered Price**_____

   Cash down payment and terms asked?_____

   How much land to be released for down payment?_____

   How firm is the seller on price and terms?_____

   Is the property reasonably priced?_____

6. What factor would cause the price and terms to be negotiated?_____
   _____

7. What terms should be offered?_____ _____

8. Can portions of the land be released without full payment?_____

9. Indicate contingency clauses to be included in the purchase agreement. These
   contingencies are concerns that would cause the contract to be terminated with cause.

Soils Report	_____	FHA/VA Approval	_____
Engineering Study	_____	Environmental Study	_____
Final Plat Approval	_____	Water /Sewer Allocation	_____
Number of Lots	_____	Availability of Utilities	_____
Access	_____	Easements	_____
Zoning	_____	Annexation	_____
Condemnation	_____	Recordation of Plat	_____
Building Permits	_____	Other	_____

Figure 1-9. Land Purchase Checklist.

LAND ACQUISITION CONTRACT OUTLINE

1. General: Buyer and Seller
2. Mutual Agreement to Buy and Sell
3. Description of Property
   a. legal description
   b. address, lot, block, municipality
   c. subdivision plat
4. Purchase Price
   a. amount: lump sum, per lot, per acre
   b. payment: method and terms
   c. security for unpaid balance
   d. releases
   e. subordination clauses
   f. optional clauses
5. Warranties of Seller
6. Contract Contingency clauses
   a. zoning
   b. building permits
   c. regulatory permits
   d. water or sewer availability
   e. other clauses
7. Inspections of property
   a. engineering studies
   b. soils investigation
   c. environmental assessment
   d. topographical and boundary surveys
8. Title Objections
9. Closing: Time
10. Condition and Possession of the property
11. Default Provisions
12. Earnest money
13. Commissions
14. Conditions of Closing
15. Assignments
16. Notice Provisions
17. Survival of Contract
18. Special Stipulations
19. Execution of Contract

Figure 1-10. Land Acquisition Contract Outline.

MANAGEMENT PROFORMA - PROBABLE CASE

Sources of Cash		Year 1	Year 2	Year 3	Total
Number of Closings		6	36	2	44
Avg. Price $191,397		$1,148,382	$6,890,288	$382,794	$8,353,259
Sale of 25% Interest at					
$25,000 per share: 10 Shares		$250,000	$0	$0	$250,000
Total Cash		**$1,398,382**	**$6,890,288**	**$382,794**	**$8,603,259**
Uses of Cash	**Per Unit**				
Architect	$227	$2,000	$8,000	$0	$10,000
Engineer	$2,409	$51,500	$54,500	$0	$106,000
Land	$15,000	$45,000	$585,000	$30,000	$660,000
Land Development	$22,000	$545,000	$423,000	$0	$968,000
Offsite Improvements	$0	$0	$0	$0	$0
Home Construction Costs	$103,280	$1,134,939	$3,323,601	$85,775	$4,544,315
Closing Costs	$500	$3,000	$18,000	$1,000	$22,000
Warranty Service	$500	$500	$16,000	$5,500	$22,000
Project Overhead	$5,068	$68,605	$147,404	$7,000	$223,009
Real Estate Commissions	$3,781	$20,904	$137,804	$7,656	$166,364
Sales and Marketing	$3,837	$91,989	$76,832	$0	$168,821
General and Administrative	$5,659	$32,405	$206,708	$11,484	$250,597
Finance, Insurance, Tax,...	$5,926	$115,750	$140,000	$5,000	$260,750
Interest/ Bank Debt(10%)	$2,454	$34,300	$73,667	$0	$107,967
Operating Uses of Cash	$170,641	$2,145,892	$5,210,516	$153,415	$7,509,823
Cash Flow from Operations		($747,510)	$1,679,772	$229,379	$1,093,436
Loan Proceeds From Bank		$1,705,000	$3,747,670	$0	$5,452,670
Loan Repayments		($835,000)	$1,069,124,154	$0	($5,452,670)
Return of Principal		$0	($250,000)	$0	($250,000)
Net Cash Flow		$122,490	$559,772	$229,379	$911,641
Total Profit Distribution					
Investors 25%					**$227,910**
Company 75%					**$683,731**
Total Profit Distribution					**$911,641**
Outstanding Bank at Period		$870,000	$0	$0	
Outstanding Invest at Period		$250,000	$0	$0	
Cumulative Cash Balance		$122,490	$682,262	$911,641	

Figure 2-1. Management Pro Forma: Probable Case.

Management Proforma: Conservative Case		Year 1	Year 2	Year 3	Total
Sources of Cash		Year 1	Year 2	Year 3	Total
Number of Closings		6	26	12	44
Average Price $185,000		$1,110,000	$4,810,000	$2,220,000	$8,140,000
Sale of 25% Interest at					
$25,000/share: 10 Shares		$250,000	$0	$0	$250,000
Total Cash		$1,360,000	$4,810,000	$2,220,000	$8,390,000
Uses of Cash	Per Unit				
Architect	$222	$2,000	$8,000	$0	$10,000
Engineer	$2,409	$51,500	$54,500	$0	$106,000
Land	$15,000	$45,000	$585,000	$30,000	$660,000
Land Development	$22,000	$545,000	$423,000	$0	$968,000
Off-site Improvements	$0	$0	$0	$0	$0
Home Construction Costs	$103,280	$1,134,939	$3,323,601	$85,775	$4,544,315
Closing Costs	$500	$3,000	$18,000	$1,000	$22,000
Warranty Service	$500	$500	$16,000	$5,500	$22,000
Project Overhead	$5,068	$68,605	$147,404	$7,000	$223,009
Real Estate Commissions	$3,781	$20,904	$137,804	$7,656	$166,364
Sales and Marketing	$3,837	$91,989	$76,832	$0	$168,821
General and Administrative	$5,659	$32,405	$206,708	$11,484	$250,597
Finance, Attorney, Insurance, Tax, etc.	$5,926	$115,750	$140,000	$5,000	$260,750
Interest on Bank Debt(10%)	$2,454	$34,300	$73,667	$0	$107,967
					$7,509,823
Operating Uses of Cash	$170,641	$2,145,892	$5,210,516	$153,415	$7,509,823
Cash Flow form Operations		($785,892)	($400,516)	$2,066,585	$880,177
Loan Proceeds From Bank		$1,705,000	$2,747,670	$1,000,000	$5,452,670
Loan Repayments		($835,000)	($2,300,000)	$1,071,424,154	$1,068,289,154
Return of Principal		$0	$0	($250,000)	($250,000)
Net Cash Flow		$84,108	$47,154	$229,379	$360,641
Total Profit Distribution					
Investors 25%					**$90,160**
Company 75%					**$270,481**
Total Profit Distribution					**$360,641**
Outstanding Bank at Period		$870,000	$1,317,670	$0	
Outstanding Invest at Period		$250,000	$250,000	$0	
Cumulative Cash Balance		$84,108	$131,262	$360,641	

Figure 2-2. Management Pro Forma: Conservative Case.

COMPREHENSIVE PROJECT ACTIVITY SCHEDULE

DAY   ACTIVITY

Land Acquisition

000–030   Project Evaluation

030–090   Access Market, Competition, Labor Force, etc.

000–030   Regulatory Analysis

030–090   Site Analysis, Technical Review of Site Information

060–120   Product Development and Density Analysis

120–135   Prepare a Proposed Land Development Budget

135–135   Prepare Project Proforma

000–180   Negotiation Strategy, Prepare Contract for Land Purchase

Conceptual Design

150–180   Select Design Team Members

030–120   Indepth Regulatory Review with Design Team

150–180   Finalize Design Development Program for the Project

180–210   Prepare Conceptual Land Plans for Review

180–210   Develop Preliminary Housing Design Program

180–270   Develop Project Theme, Market and Sales Programs

220–220   Select Land Plan and Finalize Housing Concepts

210–240   Complete Conceptual Engineering Design

210–240   Complete Design Development Architectural Plans

240–270   Prepare Conceptual Cost Estimate and Budgets

270–270   Complete Project Proforma

240–270   Establish Project Goals, Schedule and Opening Date

240–270   Review Construction Specifications for Project

280–Completion Monitor Overall Project Schedule

Figure 3-1. Comprehensive Project Activity Schedule.

Preliminary and Final Design

240–270	Negotiate Professional Services Contracts
270–390	Complete Final Engineering Design Plans
270–390	Complete Final Architectural Design Plans
330–390	Complete landscaping Design Plans
360–390	Prepare Preliminary Cost Estimate and Budgets
390–390	Prepare Project Proforma

Regulatory Process

240–390	Schedule Planning Sessions for Regulatory Strategy
390–480	Municipal and County Planning Boards
390–480	Municipal Planner and Engineering Review Meetings
390–450	Water and Sewer Municipal Review
390–450	Soil Conservation District Permit Review
450–480	County Water and sewer District Reviews
480–540	State Agency Reviews
390–570	Regional Agency Reviews
280–390	Federal Agency Reviews
330–390	Citizen Participation Program
480–540	HOA Documents, Warranty Registrations

Model Center

480–510	Construction and Sales Sequence Program
430–480	Model Center Design Concept and Approach
430–480	Prepare Model Center Site Plan
430–480	Complete Model Center, Entry Feature Landscaping Plan
480–510	Complete Signage Design
390–480	Complete Interior Design Program
480–540	Obtain Regulatory Permits for Model Center
480–510	Prepare Model Center Budget
480–540	Complete Sales Brochures, Ad Campaign, Billboards

Figure 3-1. Comprehensive Project Activity Schedule—*continued.*

480–540	Complete Scale Model of Project
80–540	Prepare Final Project Proforma and Budget

Construction Process

480–510	Prepare Land Development Schedule
480–540	Complete Land Development Bid Process
520–540	Complete Land Development Negotiations and Contracts
480–510	Unit Production Schedules
480–540	Unit Construction Contracts
540–630	Model Center land Development
480–540	Install Temporary Sales Trailer at Site
540–570	Install Sales Displays and Trailer Interiors
540–570	Complete Landscaping and Signage for Sales Trailer
570–570	Preconstruction Sales Opening
590–750	Model Center Construction
720–770	Complete Model Center Landscaping and Hardscape
720–770	Complete Model Center Model Interiors
780–780	Grand Opening

Project Development

As needed	Complete Special Land Development Projects
To Completion	Land Development
To Completion	Sales
To Completion	Unit Construction
To Completion	Closings
To Completion	Municipal Acceptance of Infrastrucutre
To Completion	Homeowners Association Transition

Figure 3-1. Comprehensive Project Activity Schedule—*continued*.

MULTIPLE PROJECT MASTER SCHEDULE

# Units	Project	Land Plan		Engineering		Regulatory Process				Land Development				Unit Construction		Comments
		Start	Comp	Prelim Comp	Final Comp	Prelim Submit	Plan Appr	Final Subm	Plans Appr	Contract Comp	Start	Pad	Comp	Start	1st CO	
13	Mark Mills	6/7	7/7	8/17	8/17	8/18	2/9	8/18	2/9	3/9	4/9	7/9	12/12	7/10	12/10	

Figure 3-2. Multiple Project Master Schedule.

INDIVIDUAL PROJECT MASTER SCHEDULE

Project:_____   DUE DATES

Project Planning and Subdivision Concept	4/02
File for Wetlands Permits	4/02
Start Prelimianry Improvement Plans	4/15
Submit Preliminary Improvement Plans and Plat	6/02
Draft Preliminary HOA for Storm-water Facilities	6/02
Submit Preliminary Plans to State DOT	6/06
Development Review Committee Meeting for Preliminary Plans	6/19
Start Preparation of Final Improvement Plans and Plat	6/20
Design Development Plans for Product	6/27
Planning and Zoning Meeting for Preliminary Application	6/28
County Planning Board	7/19
Complete Final Engineering Plans and Plat	7/21
File for State Permits; Environmental, Traffic, Sewer, Water, etc.	7/25
Complete Final Architectural Working Drawings	8/12
Complete Construction Drawing Revisions	9/15
Forward Drawings to Construction Personnel	9/23
Forward Drawings to Sales	9/23
State Permits Due	9/26
Submit Final HOA Documents for State Review	9/26
Submit Final Plat and Improvement Plans to Planning Board	9/26
Development Review Committee meeting for Final Application	10/06
Planning and Zoning Board meeting	10/31
County Planning Board meeting	11/14
Start Land Development	11/15
Record Final Subdivision Plat	11/23
Submit for Building Permits - models	11/24
Start Sales	11/24
Start Construction of First Unit	1/24

NOTE: If any of the governmental and submittal dates are missed, the project will be
         delayed one month.

COMMENTS:_____

_____

_____

Figure 3-3. Individual Project Master Schedule.

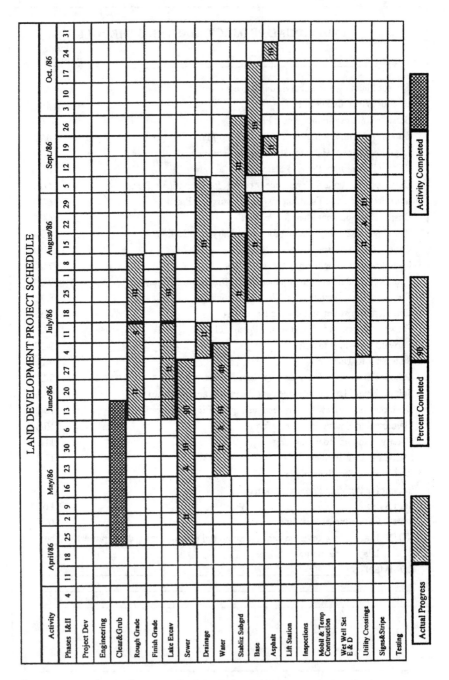

Figure 3-4. Land Development Project Schedule.

HOUSING INVENTORY REPORT

Month	Starts Orig Budg	Starts Actual Forcst	Starts Prior Year	Completions Orig Budg	Completions Act Forcst	Completions Prior Year	Closings Orig Budg	Closings Act Forcst	Closings Prior Year	Inventory Unsold Comp	Inventory Unsold Under Const	Inventory Sold Comp	Inventory Sold Under Const	Inventory Total Comp	Inventory Total Under Const	Net Orders Orig Budg	Net Orders Act Forcst	Net Orders Prior Year	Order Backlog Orig Budg	Order Backlog Act Forcst
Balance	–	–	–	–	–	–	–	–	–	–	–	–	–	49	25					54
Jan	18	3	3	8	5	4	18	14	4	27	7	13	16	40	23	30	10	7	25	50
Feb	29	13	6	8	10	8	20	10	6	30	6	10	20	40	26	41	16	10	25	56
Mar	32	10	8	8	8	3	23	4	6	34	2	10	26	44	28	40	20	20	22	72
Apr	28	27	9	18	7	6	18	5	2	36	1	10	47	46	48	35	18	12	20	85
May	33	16	15	29	7	1	24	10	4	30	2	13	55	43	57	37	20	15	18	95
June	41	14	12	32	12	10	32	15	4	30	2	10	57	40	59	28	16	30	18	96
July	30	8	32	28	16	12	21	16	7	29	2	11	49	40	51	19	11	9	22	91
Aug	30	13	24	33	13	9	21	9	12					44	51	13	14	9	25	96
Sept	35	10	13	41	16	10	26	13	7					47	45	13	16	11	28	99
Oct	10	22	8	30	20	18	23	36	14					31	47	16	26	8	29	89
Nov	10	28	8	30	40	25	33	34	19					37	35	21	28	7	29	83
Dec	10	28	10	35	46	34	41	34	25					49	17	19	26	3	28	75
Total	306	192	148	300	200	140	300	200	110					49	17	312	221	141	28	75

Figure 3-5. Housing Inventory Report.

PROFESSIONAL SERVICE AGREEMENT

THIS AGREEMENT made this   day of   19 by and between   , having an address of

, hereinafter called "   " and hereinafter called "CONTRACTOR"

For and in consideration of the mutual covenants herein contained the parties hereto do hereby agree as follows:

The Contractor agrees, as an independent contractor, to furnish such labor and/or equipment and/or materials and/or to perform such services as may be specified in any Addendum Schedule executed by the parties and ssued in connection with this Agreement.

All designs, drawings, specifications, technical data, and other instruments produced by Contractor in the performance of this Agreement shall be the sole property of and is vested with all rights therein of whatever kind and however created, whether by common law, statutory law, or by equity. Contractor agrees that shall have access at all reasonable time to inspect and make copies of all notes, designs, drawings, specifications and other technical data pertaining to the work to be performed under this Agreement.

Contractor shall comply with existing ordinances and rules of municipality where work is done, and shall comply with all County, State and Federal laws pertaining to such work. Contractor shall also comply with all State Safety Ordinances, Federal OSHA Standards and Company Programs.

The Contractor agrees to and does hereby indemnify and save harmless from and against any and all loss, damage, claims, actions, liability and expense in contract or in tort, in connection with loss of life, bodily injury and/or property damage occurring on or about or arising out of those areas of the Project occupied by him or under his control, or wherever arising if occasioned wholly or in part by any act or omission of, or any defect in workmanship, services or material furnished by the Contractor, his subcontractors, sub-subcontractors, or any subcontractors or sub-subcontractors of any of them, or by his or their agents, servants, employees or materialmen, whether the same arise during the progress of the work or at any time subsequent to completion of the work.

"Contractor", shall provide and maintain in full force in connection with performance of insurance operation Worker's Compensation Insurance, comprehensive General Liability (including but not limited to, contractural products/completed operations including broad

Figure 5-1. Professional Service Agreement.

form property damage and personal injury coverage), with limits of $1,000,000 Combined Single Limit (CSL) for both bodily injury and property damage. An umbrella policy with a minimum limit of $2,000,000 must be excess above the underlying $1,000,000 CSL. In addition, automobile liability must be maintained with a $1,000,000 CSL Limit and be scheduled in the umbrella policy. All insurance shall be in force until expiratoin of the contract agreement. Said policies shall contain a provision that the same will not be cancelled or materially changed without thirty (30) days prior written notice to. Contractor and/or contractor's sub-contractor shall deliver to certificates of the workmen's comprehensive general liability and the legal liability property damage policies showing due issuance of such insurance. Contractor agrees that business operations shall not begin unless and until such certificates covering same are delivered.

An engineer, architect, surveyor or any other outside professional service contracted by must provide professional errors and omissions insurance with a minimum of $1,000,000 limit and must maintain this coverage for two (2) years after the completion of said work. All other conditions set forth must also be evidenced in addition to professional liability.

Insurance Company must be at minimum an AM Best "A+" rated carrier and licensed to do business in the State of .

Contractor is engaged by only for the purposes and to the extent set forth in this Agreement, and his relation to, during the term of this Agreement, shall not be considered under the provisions of this Agreement as having an employee status or being entitled to participate in any benefits for regular employees.

Either party hereto may terminate this Agreement for any reason upon THIRTY (30) DAYS prior written notice given to the other party by certified or registered mail and sent to the address of said other party indicated hereinabove.

Any waiver, alteration, or modification of any of the provisions of this Agreement shall not be valid unless in writing and signed by the parties.

IN WITNESS WHEREOF, the undersigned parties have hereby caused this Agreement to be duly executed on the day and year first above written.

COMPANY:_____TITLE:_____DATE:_____
CONTRACTOR:_____ TITLE:_____DATE:_____

Figure 5-1. Professional Service Agreement—*continued.*

SITE FEASIBILITY AND SURVEY CONTRACT ADDENDUM

XYZ CORPORATION ADDENDUM #_____

STREET ADDRESS DATE:_____

CITY, STATE, ZIP PAGE:_____ OF _____

FORMING PART OF CONTRACT # _____ DATED:_____

BETWEEN XYZ AND_____

FOR WORK AT_____

CATEGORY OF WORK: SITE FEASIBILITY AND SURVEY

NOTE:THE STATED PRICE BELOW INCLUDES ALL FEDERAL, STATE AND LOCAL TAXES

<u>DESCRIPTION AND SCOPE OF WORK</u>:

The consultant named above shall perform the following tasks for _____
_____ project at <u>City, State</u>. This scope of services limits itself to a site feasibility study, survey and preparation of an Exhibit "B" for the Department of Community Affairs, including a site analysis with consideration of XYZ's projected type of housing product.

XYZ Corporation is considering a _____ housing product. The size of the site is approximately+/-   ac.

With all of the explained above, the consultant shall proceed to:

<u>Task I - - Survey</u>

A. The Consultant shall perform a boundary and topographic survey including, but not being limited to, the following:

    1. Existing elevations on site

    2. Location and elevation of any existing swales

    3. Location and elevations of any existing ponds

    4. Water surface elevations of the adjacent waterway

    5. Elevation of Quesada Avenue, at center line, edge of pavement and R/W line

    6. Location and elevations of any drainage structures

    7. Location of all existing utilities

       The survey shall extend 50' beyond the site boundaries and shall be included on a sketch at 1" = 50' scale. (1 ft. = 30 centimeters; 1 acre = 0.4 hectares)

CONTRACTOR:_____ XYZ CORPORATION:_____

BY:_____ BY: _____

TITLE:_____ DATE:_____ TITLE:_____DATE:____

PREPARED BY:_____ DATE:_____

REVIEWED BY:_____ DATE:_____

Figure 5-2. Site Feasibility and Survey Contract Addendum.

CONTRACT ADDENDUM

XYZ CORPORATION   ADDENDUM #_____
STREET ADDRESS   DATE: _____
CITY, STATE ZIP   PAGE:_____OF_____
FORMING PART OF CONTRACT # _____   DATED: _____
BETWEEN XYZ AND _____
FOR WORK AT_____

CATEGORY OF WORK: SITE FEASIBILITY AND SURVEY

Task II - - Site Analysis
A. Some of the following data shall be collected from XYZ, or any public office in cases where these would not be available at XYZ. Others will be reflected on the survey performed in Task I :
    1. Comprehensive Plan*
    2. XYZ Land Plan*
    3. Vicinity Map*
    4. Zoning Map*
    5. Topography*
    6. Aerial*
    7. Utility Plans*
    8. Road and Drainage Plans*
    9. Transportation Information
    10. Subdivision Regulations*
    11. Flood Plain Information (FIA Maps)
    12. Soils
*Available information at XYZ.

B. A meeting between the consultant and XYZ's Community Director shall be arranged by XYZ. A determination of the availability of services, agency/community attitudes, regulations, requirements and an onsite physical investigation of the property shall be a part of this meeting.

    After A and B have been completed, a thorough analysis shall be effected by the consultant and implemented into TASK III.

CONTRACTOR:_____ XYZ CORPORATION_____
BY:_____BY:_____
TITLE:_____ DATE:_____TITLE:_____ DATE:____

PREPARED BY:_____ DATE:_____
REVIEWED BY:_____ DATE:_____

Figure 5-2. Site Feasibility and Survey Contract Addendum—*continued.*

CONTRACT ADDENDUM

XYZ CORPORATION   ADDENDUM # _____
STREET ADDRESS   DATE: _____
CITY, STATE ZIP   PAGE:_____OF_____
FORMING PART OF CONTRACT # _____   DATED: _____
BETWEEN XYZ AND _____
FOR WORK AT_____

CATEGORY OF WORK: SITE FEASIBILITY AND SURVEY

TASK III -- FEASIBILITY REPORT

Use site analysis information and survey data to evaluate the site for development potential. Prepare written report which shall include, but not be limited to, the following information and supplemented by key exhibits, maps or plans.

1. Location of the property
2. Legal description of the property
3. Size of property in acres
4. Brief background history of the land
5. Development status (according to D.S.P./XYZ agreement of _____)
6. Projected number and density, based on desired product by XYZ. Also, discuss procedure of subdivision regulations and site plan review process, including time frames.
7. Define what portions, if any, of the land may be excluded from computing the net buildable acreage.
8. Length of frontage; Depth of Parcel
9. Zoning requirements; Setbacks and other open space required:
   a) Building restrictions
   b) Architectural restrictions
   c) Local restrictions
10. Existing and anticipated easements or rights of ways affecting the property. Provide source of information.
11. Evaluation of available topography and fill requirements
12. Evaluation of soils. Soil tests will be provided by XYZ.

CONTRACTOR:_____XYZ CORPORATION_____
BY:_____BY:_____
TITLE:_____ DATE:_____ TITLE:_____DATE:_____

PREPARED BY:_____ DATE:_____
REVIEWED BY:_____ DATE:_____

Figure 5-2. Site Feasibility and Survey Contract Addendum—*continued.*

CONTRACT ADDENDUM

XYZ CORPORATION   ADDENDUM #_____
STREET ADDRESS   DATE: _____
CITY, STATE ZIP   PAGE:_____OF_____
FORMING PART OF CONTRACT # _____ DATED: _____
BETWEEN XYZ AND _____
FOR WORK AT_____

CATEGORY OF WORK: SITE FEASIBILITY AND SURVEY

TASK III -- FEASIBILITY REPORT (Cont'd)

13. Description of existing vegetation
14. Impact of floodplains: Construction problems, filling, etc.
15. Water Management (storm drainage) requirements, and identification of agencies with jurisdiction:
    a) On-site
    b) Off-site
16. Water & Sewer:
    a) Check availability and utility plant capacity
    b) Discuss if any special improvements are needed
    c) Consideration of a sewer package treatment plant and its approximate cost
    d) Consideration of a water package plant and its approximate cost
17. Other Utilities: Check availability of gas, telephone, power and cable TV, and identify supplying companies
18. Accessibility
    a) Condition, ownership and improvement requirements of frontage road
    b) Existing and anticipated traffic flow problem
    c) Acceptability of entrances to access road
    d) Future Roads
        1) Right of way needed
        2) New road planned
        3) Connections to existing or future adjacent developments
19. Nature of surrounding land and type of surrounding zoning
20. Anticipated off-site improvements -- estimated costs, if any

CONTRACTOR:_____ XYZ CORPORATION_____
BY:_____ BY: _____
TITLE:_____ DATE:_____TITLE:_____DATE:____

PREPARED BY:_____ DATE:_____
REVIEWED BY:_____ DATE:_____

Figure 5-2. Site Feasibility and Survey Contract Addendum—*continued.*

CONTRACT ADDENDUM

XYZ CORPORATION   ADDENDUM #_____
STREET ADDRESS   DATE: _____
CITY, STATE ZIP   PAGE:_____OF_____
FORMING PART OF CONTRACT # _____   DATED: _____
BETWEEN XYZ AND _____
FOR WORK AT_____

CATEGORY OF WORK: SITE FEASIBILITY AND SURVEY

TASK III -- FEASIBILITY REPORT (Cont'd)
    21. Environmental concerns and/or impact
    22. Attitude of citizens, regulating officials, elected officials and others
    23. Preliminary ideas on ways to overcome identified restrictions
    24. Outstanding reasons for developing the site
    25. Outstanding reasons for not developing the site at this time
    26. Recommendation

At a scale adequate for presentation, the written report shall be accompanied by blown up key exhibits, maps or plans. Boards 24" x 36" minimum size are recommended. 1 inch = 25 millimeters

TASK IV -- PRESENTATION

Provide XYZ with 5 copies of the Feasibility Report (TASK III) and 5 copies of D.S.P. Exhibit "B" (TASK IV). Note: For the preparation of TASK IV, the consultant shall use the same exhibits and other information included in TASK III. However, information in the Feasibility Report (TASK III) will include more than required for TASK IV.

FEES

For professional services to be rendered for the above and based on estimated hours to be spent by principal and staff, the consultant shall charge a maximum up-set fee of:

    1) TASK I, SURVEY_____ $_____
    2) TASKS II., III. and IV _____ $_____

                                    TOTAL $_____

CONTRACTOR:_____ XYZ CORPORATION_____
BY:_____ BY:_____
TITLE:_____ DATE:_____ TITLE:_____DATE:____

PREPARED BY:_____ DATE:_____
REVIEWED BY:_____ DATE:_____

Figure 5-2. Site Feasibility and Survey Contract Addendum—*continued.*

CONTRACT ADDENDUM

XYZ CORPORATION   ADDENDUM #_____
STREET ADDRESS   DATE: _____
CITY, STATE ZIP   PAGE:_____OF_____
FORMING PART OF CONTRACT # _____   DATED: _____
BETWEEN XYZ AND _____
FOR WORK AT_____

CATEGORY OF WORK: SITE FEASIBILITY AND SURVEY

GENERAL:

A. The consultant shall not subcontract out any work outlined in this agreement without prior approval by XYZ.

B. The consultant will assist XYZ through attendance at meetings with regulatory agencies in preparation of the site analysis and feasibility report, if required.

C. The scope of services shall be completed within 15 calendar days upon notice to proceed

D. XYZ reserves the right to stop the work at any moment and remunerate according to the completion of the work up to that moment.

E. Compensation -- XYZ agrees to compensate the consultant for the tasks outlined in the scope of services included herein. This shall be paid by XYZ upon approval of the report, survey and exhibits by XYZ.

F. Consultant to indicate method of payment.

CONTRACTOR:_____ XYZ CORPORATION_____
BY:_____BY:_____
TITLE:_____ DATE:_____TITLE:_____ DATE:____

PREPARED BY:_____DATE:_____
REVIEWED BY:_____ DATE:_____

Figure 5-2. Site Feasibility and Survey Contract Addendum—*continued.*

CONTRACT ADDENDUM

XYZ CORPORATION   ADDENDUM #_____
STREET ADDRESS   DATE: _____
CITY, STATE ZIP   PAGE:_____OF_____
FORMING PART OF CONTRACT # _____   DATED: _____
BETWEEN XYZ AND _____
FOR WORK AT_____

CATEGORY OF WORK: SITE FEASIBILITY AND SURVEY

GENERAL: (Cont'd)

G. Service authorized by XYZ other than those specifically outlined in the scope of services shall be considered additional services. Additional compensation shall be mutually agreed upon by XYZ and the consultant and shall be invoiced at an hourly rate of $_____ for principal and $_____ for staff.

H. XYZ shall reimburse the consultant for all out-of-pocket expenses directly chargeable to the project, at actual costs incurred. Such charges shall be itemized and included in the monthly invoices for time charges. Typical reimbursable expenses include travel, lodging, meals, printing costs, long distance telephone calls and other out-of-pocket expenses.

NO GUARANTEE OF THE NUMBER OF UNITS TO BE RELEASED TO THE SUBCONTRACTOR IS MADE OR IMPLIED. AUTHORIZATION TO PROCEED WITH WORK UNDER THIS CONTRACT ADDENDUM WILL BE FORMALLY ISSUED BY THE DIRECTOR OF OPERATIONS IN THE FORM A WRITTEN RELEASE OF UNITS FOR CONSTRUCTION. PROFESSIONAL SERVICES WOULD BE RELEASED BY THE DIRECTOR OF PROJECT DEVELOPMENT.

CONTRACTOR:_____ XYZ CORPORATION:_____
BY:_____BY:_____
TITLE:_____ DATE:_____ TITLE:_____DATE:____

PREPARED BY:_____ DATE:_____
REVIEWED BY:_____ DATE:_____

Figure 5-2. Site Feasibility and Survey Contract Addendum—*continued.*

SITE PLANNING CONTRACT

CONTRACT ADDENDUM

XYZ CORPORATION
STREET ADDRESS
CITY, STATE, ZIP
FORMING PART OF CONTRACT # _____ DATED:_____
BETWEEN XYZ AND_____
FOR WORK AT_____

ADDENDUM #_____
DATE:_____
PAGE:_____ OF _____

CATEGORY OF WORK: SITE PLANNING CONTRACT

NOTE: THE STATED PRICE BELOW INCLUDES ALL FEDERAL, STATE
   AND LOCAL TAXES.

DESCRIPTION & SCOPE OF WORK:

The consultant named above shall perform the following tasks for Tracts #. Project Name
at City, State. This scope of services limits itself to site planning, with consideration of
XYZ's projected type of housing product, and other physical and regulatory constraints.

XYZ is considering _____ housing product. The size of
the site is approximately ±____ acres. Maximum allowed density is desired.

All of the above shall be in accordance with all of the requirements of the City of _____,
in respect to its subdivision and zoning regulations and site plan approval process.

The consultant shall ensure that all of the site planning to be performed shall be consistent,
in concept, with the design criteria of the stormwater management agency(s). It shall be
the consultant's responsibility to check all the pertinent regulation requirements and
ensure that all have been considered and reflected on the conceptual site plan.

CONTRACTOR:_____ XYZ CORPORATION_____
BY:_____ BY:_____
TITLE: _____DATE:_____ TITLE:_____DATE:_____

Figure 5-3. Site Planning Contract.

CONTRACT ADDENDUM

XYZ CORPORATION   ADDENDUM #_____
STREET ADDRESS   DATE:_____
CITY, STATE, ZIP   PAGE:_____ OF _____
FORMING PART OF CONTRACT # _____ DATED:_____
BETWEEN XYZ AND_____
FOR WORK AT_____

CATEGORY OF WORK: SITE PLANNING CONTRACT (Cont'd)

With all of the explained above, the consultant shall proceed to:

I. SITE PLANNING
    Prepare three (3) planning concepts for the site. These schemes shall be
    compatible with the overall parameters set by the Department of Project
    Development of XYZ in respect to the proposed housing product and shall
    graphically define the land use, including, but not being limited to:
    A. Building locations
    B. Open space
    C. Orientation
    D. Amenities
    E. Conceptual storm-water management
    F. Access points
    G. Topographic constraints   (If any)
    H. Flood prone areas (If any)
    I. Other physical problem areas (If any)
    J. Easements (If any)
    K. Circulation network (Automobile & pedestrian)

NOTES: 1. Each scheme shall be subdivided into four (4) phases, which shall be inter-
          connected with each other, in order to adequately provide for sequential
          development.
       2. Each of the three (3) schemes shall be attractively rendered and colored.

CONTRACTOR:_____ XYZ CORPORATION_____
BY:_____ BY: _____
TITLE:_____ DATE:_____ TITLE:_____DATE:_____

PREPARED BY:_____ DATE:_____
REVIEWED BY:_____ DATE:_____

Figure 5-3. Site Planning Contract—*continued.*

CONTRACT ADDENDUM

XYZ CORPORATION   ADDENDUM #_____
STREET ADDRESS   DATE:_____
CITY, STATE, ZIP   PAGE:_____ OF _____
FORMING PART OF CONTRACT # _____ DATED:_____
BETWEEN XYZ AND_____
FOR WORK AT_____

CATEGORY OF WORK: SITE PLANNING CONTRACT

DESCRIPTION & SCOPE OF WORK (Cont'd)

3. Each of the three (3) schemes shall state the following information:
   a) Name of project
   b) Location
   c) Existing zoning
   d) Acreage (total and per phase)
   e) Density allowed
   f) Density provided
   g) Number of units (total and per phase)
   h) Area and percentage covered by impervious surfaces (total and specific)
   i) Maximum lot coverage allowed
   j) Maximum lot coverage provided
   k) Open space required
   l) Open space provided
   m) Setbacks required

4. Originals shall be given to the Department of Project Development. The consultant shall keep a set of prints for future reference.

FEES:
For professional services to be rendered for the above and based on estimated hours to be spent by principal and staff, the consultant shall charge a maximum up-set fee of:

$_____

CONTRACTOR:_____ XYZ CORPORATION_____
BY:_____BY: _____
TITLE:_____ DATE:_____ TITLE:_____DATE:_____

PREPARED BY:_____ DATE:_____
REVIEWED BY:_____ DATE:_____

Figure 5-3. Site Planning Contract—*continued.*

CONTRACT ADDENDUM

XYZ CORPORATION   ADDENDUM #_____
STREET ADDRESS   DATE:_____
CITY, STATE, ZIP   PAGE:_____ OF _____
FORMING PART OF CONTRACT # _____ DATED:_____
BETWEEN XYZ AND_____
FOR WORK AT_____

CATEGORY OF WORK: SITE PLANNING

DESCRIPTION AND SCOPE OF WORK: (Cont'd)

GENERAL:

A.   There shall not be any repeat fees involved in this contract.

B.   XYZ reserves the right to reuse the construction documents in any other site or community without having to give any additional compensation to the consultant.

C.   XYZ reserves the right of ownership of the construction documents, as defined in Paragraph #2 of the Professional Service Agreement signed between the consultant and XYZ.

D.   The consultant shall not subcontract out any work outlined in this agreement without prior approval by XYZ.

E.   The consultant will assist XYZ, through attendance at meetings with regulatory agencies in preparation of the construction documents, if required.

F.   XYZ reserves the right to stop the work at any moment and remunerate according to the completion of the work up to that moment.

G.   Compensation - XYZ agrees to compensate the consultant for the work outlined in the scope of services included herein. This shall be paid by XYZ upon approval of the site plans by XYZ.

CONTRACTOR:_____XYZ CORPORATION_____
BY:_____ BY: _____
TITLE:_____ DATE:_____ TITLE:_____DATE:_____

PREPARED BY:_____ DATE:_____
REVIEWED BY:_____DATE:_____

Figure 5-3. Site Planning Contract—*continued*.

CONTRACT ADDENDUM

XYZ CORPORATION   ADDENDUM #_____
STREET ADDRESS   DATE:_____
CITY, STATE, ZIP   PAGE:_____ OF _____
FORMING PART OF CONTRACT # _____ DATED:_____
BETWEEN XYZ AND_____
FOR WORK AT_____

CATEGORY OF WORK: SITE PLANNING

DESCRIPTION AND SCOPE OF WORK: (Cont'd)

GENERAL:

H.   Consultant to indicate method of payment.

I.   Service authorized by XYZ other than those specifically outlined in the scope of
       services shall be considered additional services. Additional compensation shall be
       mutually agreed upon by XYZ and the consultant and shall be invoiced at an hourly
       rate of $__see below__ for principal and $__see below__ for staff.

J.   XYZ shall reimburse the consultant for all out-of-pocket expenses directly
       chargeable to the project, at actual costs incurred. Such charges shall be itemized and
       included in the monthly invoices for time charges. Typical reimbursable expenses
       include travel, lodging, meals, printing costs, long distance telephone calls and other
       outstanding out-of-pocket expenses.

Principal $_____ Per Hour
Sr. Landscape Architect $_____ Per Hour
Landscape Architect $_____ Per Hour
Draftsman $_____ Per Hour

NO GUARANTEE OF THE NUMBER OF UNITS TO BE RELEASED TO THE
SUBCONTRACTOR IS MADE OR IMPLIED. AUTHORIZATION TO PROCEED WITH
WORK UNDER THIS CONTRACT ADDENDUM WILL BE FORMALLY ISSUED BY
THE DIRECTOR OF OPERATIONS IN THE FORM OF A WRITTEN RELEASE OF
UNITS FOR CONSTRUCTION. PROFESSIONAL SERVICES WOULD BE RELEASED
BY THE MANAGER OF PROJECT DEVELOPMENT.

CONTRACTOR:_____XYZ CORPORATION_____
BY:_____ BY: _____
TITLE:_____ DATE:_____ TITLE:_____DATE:_____

PREPARED BY:_____ DATE:_____
REVIEWED BY:_____ DATE:_____

Figure 5-3. Site Planning Contract—*continued.*

ENGINEERING SERVICES

CONTRACT ADDENDUM

XYZ CORPORATION   ADDENDUM #_____
STREET ADDRESS   DATE:_____
CITY, STATE, ZIP   PAGE:_____ OF _____
FORMING PART OF CONTRACT # _____ DATED:_____
BETWEEN XYZ AND_____
FOR WORK AT_____

CATEGORY OF WORK: ENGINEERING SERVICES INCLUDING PLAT, PAVING,
                  DRAINAGE, WATER & SEWER

NOTE: THE STATED PRICE BELOW INCLUDES ALL FEDERAL, STATE AND
      LOCAL TAXES

DESCRIPTION & SCOPE OF WORK:

The consultant named above shall perform the following tasks in accordance with the
project. This scope of services limits itself to site engineering including plat, paving and
drainage and utilities drawings and calculations, appropriately signed and sealed,
necessary for approximately ±48 acres of land proposed for residential use.

The above acreage will have the following housing product:

_____

_____

All of the above shall be in accordance with all of the requirements of _____County, in
respect to its subdivision and zoning regulations and site plan approval process. And also
in accordance with all the other agencies with jurisdiction in the project in respect to
storm-water management and utilities. It shall be the consultant's responsibility to check
all the pertinent regulation requirements and ensure that all have been met and that each
submission is complete, with all required items included, so as to obtain all permits.

CONTRACTOR:_____ XYZ CORPORATION_____
BY:_____ BY: _____
TITLE:_____ DATE:_____ TITLE:_____DATE:_____

PREPARED BY:_____ DATE:_____
REVIEWED BY:_____ DATE:_____

Figure 5-4. Engineering Services.

CONTRACT ADDENDUM

XYZ CORPORATION   ADDENDUM #_____
STREET ADDRESS   DATE:_____.
CITY, STATE, ZIP   PAGE:_____ OF _____
FORMING PART OF CONTRACT # _____ DATED:_____
BETWEEN XYZ AND_____
FOR WORK AT_____

CATEGORY OF WORK: ENGINEERING SERVICES (Cont'd)

Keeping within the parameters fixed on the schematic plan approved by XYZ concerning the site plan, the consultant shall render the following services:

Task I - Preliminary Design Development

1. The consultant shall prepare the preliminary plat and preliminary site work (including paving, drainage, and utility plans) for the appropriate governmental submissions in accordance with the project schedule.

2. The consultant will attend required public meetings as well as meeting with XYZ, as required, to formalize the design.

3. The consultant shall review the project with the pertinent Federal, State, Regional, and Local agencies and prepare the appropriate applications when required. The consultant will inform XYZ of the requirements imposed by the agencies. Decisions based upon the requirements will be the responsibility of XYZ. The consultant will act in an advisory role during the decision process in evaluating all governmental recommendations based upon their reviews.

4. The consultant shall finalize the preliminary drawings in accordance with review comments and suggestions so as to obtain governmental approvals.

5. The consultant shall design the water and sewer lines within the site and from the site to the existing water and sewer lines. The design shall be in accordance with the local utility standards.

CONTRACTOR:_____XYZ CORPORATION_____
BY:_____BY:_____
TITLE:_____ DATE:_____ TITLE:_____DATE:_____

PREPARED BY:_____ DATE:_____
REVIEWED BY:_____DATE:_____

Figure 5-4. Engineering Services—*continued.*

CONTRACT ADDENDUM

XYZ CORPORATION   ADDENDUM #_____
STREET ADDRESS   DATE:_____
CITY, STATE, ZIP   PAGE:_____ OF _____
FORMING PART OF CONTRACT # _____ DATED: _____
BETWEEN XYZ AND_____
FOR WORK AT_____

CATEGORY OF WORK: ENGINEERING SERVICES (Cont'd)

6. Proper coordination with XYZ Engineering and Land Development Departments shall be maintained by the consultant throughout the project for the incorporation of accepted XYZ construction standards.

7. An estimate of probable cost shall be submitted to XYZ at the completion of preliminary design development. This shall meet the construction budget approved by XYZ. In cases where the estimate is over the budget the consultant shall advise XYZ how to reduce the cost.

Task II - Final Construction Documents

1. The consultant shall prepare final engineering site work (including final paving, drainage, and utility plans), and final plat plans for the appropriate government submissions and make application for necessary approvals in accordance with the project schedule. The engineering design shall be in accordance with XYZ land development standards.

2. The consultant will work with XYZ in preparing for governmental submissions, providing the appropriate documents, applications and attending meetings as required.

3. The consultant shall finalize the construction drawings in accordance with review comments and suggestions so as to obtain governmental approvals.

4. The consultant shall make applications for obtaining the necessary Federal, State, Regional and/or Local permits required. Drawings shall be revised by the consultant, if required, because of non-compliance by any of the agencies with jurisdiction on the project at no extra charge to XYZ.

CONTRACTOR:_____ XYZ CORPORATION_____
BY:_____ BY: _____
TITLE:_____ DATE:_____ TITLE:_____DATE:_____

PREPARED BY:_____ DATE:_____
REVIEWED BY:_____ DATE:_____

Figure 5-4. Engineering Services—*continued.*

CONTRACT ADDENDUM

XYZ CORPORATION
STREET ADDRESS
CITY, STATE, ZIP
FORMING PART OF CONTRACT # _____ DATED:_____
BETWEEN XYZ AND_____
FOR WORK AT_____

ADDENDUM #_____
DATE:_____
PAGE:_____ OF _____

CATEGORY OF WORK: ENGINEERING SERVICES (Cont'd)

Task II - Final Construction Documents (Cont'd)

5. The final plat shall be prepared to be suitable for recording with bearings and dimensions of all lines of roadways, lots, easements, recreation areas and the legal dedications, according to the rules and regulations of the State of _____.

6. Reviews of progress prints shall be done so between the consultant and XYZ Project Development Department, for proper coordination and compliance of the project with XYZ's goals and objectives.

7. The consultant shall prepare a final cost estimate at the completion of final construction documents, which shall meet the approved construction budget.

8. Specifications shall be included on the drawings.

CONTRACTOR:_____   XYZ CORPORATION_____
BY:_____   BY: _____
TITLE:_____ DATE:_____   TITLE:_____DATE:_____

PREPARED BY:_____ DATE:_____
REVIEWED BY:_____ DATE:_____

Figure 5-4. Engineering Services—*continued.*

CONTRACT ADDENDUM

XYZ CORPORATION   ADDENDUM # _____
STREET ADDRESS   DATE:_____
CITY, STATE, ZIP   PAGE:_____ OF _____
FORMING PART OF CONTRACT # _____ DATED:_____
BETWEEN XYZ AND_____
FOR WORK AT_____

CATEGORY OF WORK: ENGINEERING SERVICES (Cont'd)

Task III
The consultant shall provide on-site construction observation services on as as-requested basis.

Fee schedule

I. Preliminary Design Development

  1. Preliminary Plat $_____ (Including survey for plat recording)
  2. Civil (Paving, and drainage $_____
   Utilities)
  3. Public Hearings, $_____
  4. Governmental Approvals
   & other Conferences
  5. Estimating $_____
       Total $_____

II. Final Construction Documents

  1. Final Plat $_____
  2. Civil (Paving,drainage, $_____
   Utilities)
  3. Public Hearings, $_____
   Governmental Approvals
   &other Conferences
  4. Estimating $_____
  5. Specifications $_____
       Total $_____

CONTRACTOR:_____ XYZ CORPORATION_____
BY:_____ BY: _____
TITLE:_____ DATE:_____ TITLE:_____DATE:_____

PREPARED BY:_____ DATE:_____
REVIEWED BY:_____DATE:_____

Figure 5-4. Engineering Services—*continued.*

CONTRACT ADDENDUM

XYZ CORPORATION   ADDENDUM #_____
STREET ADDRESS   DATE:_____
CITY, STATE, ZIP   PAGE:_____ OF _____
FORMING PART OF CONTRACT # _____ DATED:_____
BETWEEN XYZ AND_____
FOR WORK AT_____

CATEGORY OF WORK: ENGINEERING SERVICES (Cont'd)

III. Construction Observation

    Site Visits $_____

These shall reflect the fees per visit, and shall be as stated in Task III "on an as-requested basis" (reimbursables shall be paid extra).

GENERAL:
A. There shall not be any repeat fees involved in this contract.

B. XYZ reserves the right to reuse the construction documents in any other site or community without having to give any additional compensation to the consultant.

C. XYZ reserves the right of ownership of the construction documents, as defined in Paragraph #2 of the Professional Service Agreement signed between the consultant and XYZ.

D. The consultant shall not subcontract out any work outlined in this agreement without prior approval by XYZ.

E. The consultant will assist XYZ, through attendance at meeting with regulatory agencies in preparation of the construction documents, if required.

F. XYZ reserves the right to stop the work at any moment and remunerate according to the completion of the work up to that moment.

G. Compensation - XYZ agrees to compensate the consultant for the tasks outlined in the scope of services included herein. This shall be paid by XYZ upon approval of the construction documents.

CONTRACTOR:_____ XYZ CORPORATION_____
BY:_____ BY: _____
TITLE:_____ DATE:_____ TITLE:_____DATE:_____

PREPARED BY:_____ DATE:_____
REVIEWED BY:_____ DATE:_____

Figure 5-4. Engineering Services—*continued.*

CONTRACT ADDENDUM

XYZ CORPORATION   ADDENDUM #_____
STREET ADDRESS   DATE:_____
CITY, STATE, ZIP   PAGE:_____ OF _____
FORMING PART OF CONTRACT # _____ DATED:_____
BETWEEN XYZ AND_____
FOR WORK AT_____

CATEGORY OF WORK: ENGINEERING SERVICES

GENERAL (Cont'd):

H. Consultant to indicate method of payment.

I. Service authorized by XYZ other than those specifically outlined in the scope of services shall be considered additional services. Additional compensation shall be mutually agreed upon by XYZ and the consultant and shall be invoiced at an hourly rate of $_____ or principal, and $_____ for staff.

J. XYZ shall reimburse the consultant for all out-of-pocket expenses directly chargeable to the project, at actual costs incurred. Such charges shall be itemized and included in the monthly invoices for time charges. Typical reimbursable expenses include travel, lodging, meals, printing costs, long distance telephone calls and other out-of-pocket expenses.

NO GUARANTEE OF THE NUMBER OF UNITS TO BE RELEASED TO THE SUBCONTRACTOR IS MADE OR IMPLIED. AUTHORIZATION TO PROCEED WITH WORK UNDER THIS CONTRACT ADDENDUM WILL BE FORMALLY ISSUED BY THE DIRECTOR OF OPERATIONS IN THE FORM OF A WRITTEN RELEASE OF UNITS FOR CONSTRUCTION. PROFESSIONAL SERVICES WOULD BE RELEASED BY THE DIRECTOR OF PROJECT DEVELOPMENT.

CONTRACTOR:_____ XYZ CORPORATION_____
BY:_____ BY: _____
TITLE:_____ DATE:_____ TITLE:_____DATE:_____

PREPARED BY:_____ DATE:_____
REVIEWED BY:_____ DATE:_____

Figure 5-4. Engineering Services—*continued.*

ARCHITECTURAL WORKING DRAWINGS

CONTRACT ADDENDUM

XYZ CORPORATION   ADDENDUM #_____
STREET ADDRESS   DATE:_____
CITY, STATE, ZIP   PAGE:_____ OF _____
FORMING PART OF CONTRACT # _____ DATED:_____
BETWEEN XYZ AND_____
FOR WORK AT_____

CATEGORY OF WORK: ARCHITECTURAL WORKING DRAWINGS

NOTE: THE STATED PRICE BELOW INCLUDES ALL FEDERAL, STATE AND
      LOCAL TAXES.

DESCRIPTION & SCOPE OF WORK:

The consultant named above shall perform the following tasks for XYZ. This scope of
services limits itself to the production of construction documents (including an
architectural site plan) appropriately signed and sealed.

The above will have the following housing product:_____

All of the above shall be in accordance with all of the requirements of _____
County, in respect to the regulations of all the local government agencies. These shall be
the Building Department and the Planning and Zoning Department. Their building, fire
and zoning regulations shall be properly reflected on the construction documents as well
as compliance with their adopted county and/or national codes. The consultant shall
inform XYZ when conflicts should occur between the regulations from these local
government departments and the original XYZ design, and act in an advisory role.

CONTRACTOR:_____ XYZ CORPORATION_____
BY:_____ BY: _____
TITLE:_____ DATE:_____ TITLE:_____DATE:_____

PREPARD BY:_____ DATE:_____
REVIEWED BY:_____ DATE:_____

Figure 5-5. Architectural Working Drawings.

CONTRACT ADDENDUM

XYZ CORPORATION   ADDENDUM #_____
STREET ADDRESS   DATE:_____
CITY, STATE, ZIP   PAGE:_____ OF _____
FORMING PART OF CONTRACT # _____ DATED:_____
BETWEEN XYZ AND_____
FOR WORK AT_____

CATEGORY OF WORK: ARCHITECTURAL WORKING DRAWINGS

I. Construction Documents

   A. Prior to starting the work, the consultant shall meet with the Department of Project Development to formalize all the different design and building parameters required for the execution of the construction of this project.

   B. The consultant shall finalize the construction drawings including architectural, structural, HVAC, electrical and plumbing designs to sufficient level for building permits, negotiating contracts and construction, including the compliance with energy code. Specifications shall be provided on drawings.

   C. All dimensions shall be true and correct. If the XYZ Construction Director deems that the construction details are insufficient for the proper execution of the project, the consultant shall provide the necessary clarifications, including sketches, if necessary, in a timely manner, at no extra charge to XYZ.

   D. The consultant shall assist XYZ at any local government meeting, in any interpretation of the construction documents, if required.

   E. At submissions to _____ County staff, its Building Department, or its Planning and Zoning Department should there be indicated revisions for non-compliance with the governing building code or any other local regulation concerning planning, zoning or methods of construction, these shall be corrected by the consultant at no extra charge to XYZ.

CONTRACTOR:_____ XYZ CORPORATION_____
BY:_____ BY: _____
TITLE:_____ DATE:_____ TITLE:_____DATE:_____

PREPARED BY:_____ DATE:_____
REVIEWED BY:_____ DATE:_____

Figure 5-5. Architectural Working Drawings—*continued.*

CONTRACT ADDENDUM

XYZ CORPORATION
STREET ADDRESS
CITY, STATE, ZIP
FORMING PART OF CONTRACT # _____ DATED:_____
BETWEEN XYZ AND_____
FOR WORK AT_____

ADDENDUM #_____
DATE:_____
PAGE:_____ OF _____

CATEGORY OF WORK: ARCHITECTURAL WORKING DRAWINGS

I. Construction Documents (Cont'd)

    F. Reviews of progress prints shall be done so between the consultant and XYZ Chief Architect, for proper coordination and compliance of the project with XYZ's goals and objectives.

    G. The consultant agrees to comply with the set schedule of completion of the work necessary to file for a building permit with _____ County. This shall be set by the Department of Project Development.

II. Construction Observation

The consultant shall provide onsite construction observation on an as required basis.

III. Fees

    A. For professional services to be rendered for the above and bases on estimated hours to be spent by principal and staff, the consultant shall charge a maximum up-set fee of:

    _____.

    B. Construction Phase -- Shop Drawings $_____

    C. Construction Observation -- Site Visits $_____

These shall reflect the fees per visit, and these shall be as stated before : "On an as requested basis" (reimbursables shall be paid extra).

CONTRACTOR:_____ XYZ CORPORATION_____
BY:_____ BY: _____
TITLE:_____ DATE:_____ TITLE:_____DATE:_____

PREPARED BY:_____DATE:_____
REVIEWED BY:_____ DATE:_____

Figure 5-5. Architectural Working Drawings—*continued.*

CONTRACT ADDENDUM

XYZ CORPORATION   ADDENDUM #_____
STREET ADDRESS   DATE:_____
CITY, STATE, ZIP   PAGE:_____ OF _____
FORMING PART OF CONTRACT # _____ DATED:_____
BETWEEN XYZ AND_____
FOR WORK AT_____

CATEGORY OF WORK: ARCHITECTURAL WORKING DRAWINGS

GENERAL:

A. There shall not be any repeat fees involved in this contract.

B. XYZ reserves the right to reuse the construction documents in any other site or community without having to give any additional compensation to the consultant.

C. XYZ reserves the right of ownership of the construction documents, as defined in Paragraph #2 of the Professional Service Agreement signed between the consultant and XYZ.

D. The consultant shall not subcontract out any work outlined in this agreement without prior approval by XYZ.

E. The consultant will assist XYZ, through attendance at meetings with regulatory agencies in preparation of the construction documents, if required.

F. XYZ reserves the right to stop the work at any moment and remunerate according to the completion of the work up to that moment.

G. Compensation - XYZ agrees to compensate the consultant for the tasks outlined in the scope of services included herein. This shall be paid by XYZ upon approval of the construction documents and condominium exhibits.

H. Consultant to indicate method of payment.

CONTRACTOR:_____ XYZ CORPORATION_____
BY:_____ BY: _____
TITLE:_____ DATE:_____ TITLE:_____ DATE:_____

PREPARED BY:_____ DATE:_____
REVIEWED BY:_____ DATE:_____

Figure 5-5. Architectural Working Drawings—*continued.*

CONTRACT ADDENDUM

XYZ CORPORATION   ADDENDUM #_____
STREET ADDRESS   DATE:_____
CITY, STATE, ZIP   PAGE:_____ OF _____
FORMING PART OF CONTRACT # _____ DATED:_____
BETWEEN XYZ AND_____
FOR WORK AT_____

CATEGORY OF WORK: ARCHITECTURAL WORKING DRAWINGS

<u>GENERAL</u>: (Cont'd)

I. Service authorized by XYZ other than those specifically outlined in the scope of services shall be considered additional services. Additional compensation shall be mutually agreed upon by XYZ and the consultant and shall be invoiced at an hourly rate of $_____ for principal and $_____ for staff.

J. XYZ shall reimburse the consultant for all out-of-pocket expenses directly chargeable to the project, at actual costs incurred. Such charges shall be itemized and included in the monthly invoices for time charges. Typical reimbursable expenses include travel, lodging, meals, printing costs, long distance telephone calls and other out-of-pocket expenses.

NO GUARANTEE OF THE NUMBER OF UNITS TO BE RELEASED TO THE SUBCONTRACTOR IS MADE OR IMPLIED. AUTHORIZATION TO PROCEED WITH WORK UNDER THIS CONTRACT ADDENDUM WILL BE FORMALLY ISSUED BY THE DIRECTOR OF OPERATIONS IN THE FORM OF A WRITTEN RELEASE OF UNITS FOR CONSTRUCTION. PROFESSIONAL SERVICES WOULD BE RELEASED BY THE DIRECTOR OF PROJECT DEVELOPMENT.

CONTRACTOR:_____ XYZ CORPORATION_____
BY:_____ BY: _____
TITLE:_____ DATE:_____ TITLE:_____ DATE:_____

PREPARED BY:_____ DATE:_____
REVIEWED BY:_____ DATE:_____

Figure 5-5. Architectural Working Drawings—*continued.*

LAND DEVELOPMENT SURVEYING
SCOPE OF SERVICES

LAND DEVELOPMENT

<u>Boundary Survey</u>

Includes a research of public land records; location of existing monuments, pipes, markers, etc.; traverse establishment; boundary corner establishment; furnishing of a certified plat which shows property corners and boundary lines with noted bearings and distances as well as any existing man-made features and any other data necessitated by legal and/or public agency requirements; and, the furnishing of a written boundary description.

<u>Topographic Survey</u>

Includes field work and/or photogrammetry necessary to prepare and furnish a contour map of the tract at a scale of 1 in. = 50 ft or larger and at a contour interval of 1ft. Indicate rock outcroppings, wooded areas, streams, obvious fill areas, buildings, fence lines and any other existing features.

<u>Land Development Surveying</u>

1. <u>Control</u>
   The Surveyor shall be responsible for establishing and bringing forward all horizontal and vertical control required.

2. <u>Earthwork Staking</u>
   The Engineer shall provide one (1) complete set of stakes for mass grading the site. A complete set of stakes is considered to be road grade stakes reflecting the centerline road grade and alignment and two (2) stakes to define "house pad" for purposes of mass grading. It is assumed that the original set of stakes will be preserved and protected during the initial phase of mass grading, however, replacement of a maximum of ten percent (10%) of the total number of mass grading stakes originally set will be replaced by the Surveyor at no additional cost to the Owner.

3. <u>Utility Staking</u>
   A. <u>Storm Sewer</u>
   One (1) complete set of stakes shall be provided on an off-set determined by your Contractor. These stakes shall reflect alignment and grade and will be provided with 50 foot centers along all lines. In addition, all structures will be staked for location and grade. Cut sheets will be provided not later than the working day after the completion of the staking. Grades will be marked on the stakes provided as a part of the staking procedures.

Figure 5-6. Land Development Surveying Scope of Services.

LAND DEVELOPMENT (Cont'd)

B. Sanitary Sewer

One (1) complete set of stakes shall be provided on the off-set determined by your Contractor. These stakes shall reflect alignment and grade and shall be provided with 50 foot centers along all lines. In addition, all structures shall be staked for location and grade. House connections and clean outs (Y's, T's etc) shall be staked with a lath showing the location of the plan station. Cut sheets will be provided.

C. Water

One (1) complete set of stakes shall be provided on an off-set determined by your Contractor. These stakes shall reflect alignment and grade and will be provided with 50 foot centers along tangents and 25 foot centers along curves. Stakes shall also be provided for all tees, valves and fire hydrants. Curb line shall be staked as required sufficient to setback curb boxes. Cut sheets will be provided with grades to top of curb.

D. Electric/Telephone Crossings

Underground electric and telephone crossings of the roadways will be staked in accordance with the plans prepared by the electric and telephone companies. These plans will be provided to the Engineer by the Owner.

E. Other Utilities

It is anticipated that all other utilities will be installed without the need for field surveying.

4. Curb Staking

The Surveyor shall set one (1) complete set of alignment and grade stakes at an off-set determined by your Contractor for all curb construction. Stakes will be placed on 50 ft centers along tangents and 25 ft centers on horizontal and vertical curves. On curb returns at intersections, the P.C., P.T. and center of curve will be staked for purposes of assisting the Contractor during the construction of this item. Cut sheets will be provided.

5. Monuments

Monuments will be set in accordance with the final plat pursuant to schedules agreed to with the Owner.

6. As-Builts

The Surveyor, after completion of sanitary, storm drain, water main and fine grading will provide As-Built Plans for each section. The "As-Built" plans will be prepared in accordance with the requirements of the local ordinances.

Figure 5-6. Land Development Surveying Scope of Services—*continued.*

HOUSELINE SURVEYING
SCOPE OF SERVICES

HOUSELINE SURVEYING

1. Orientation to Outbounds:
This fee will include verifying horizontal and control to existing outbounds, to determine whether or not they are in agreement with the survey prepared. If we should find any discrepancy in the survey, we will notify your office immediately, so that you may contact the Subcontractor responsible for the survey. It will also be the developers' responsibility to provide us with a copy of the most recent survey.

2. Individual Lot Closure:
Includes verification of all metes and bounds illustrated on the Record Plan by others provided by your office.

3. Rough Grade Stakes:
Including the setting of grade stakes on lots to adequately control grading operations.

4. Lot Clearing Stakes:
Including the staking of limits of clearing at rear of houses

5. Utility Stakeout:
Including the staking of the well and septic tank locations in accordance with permit drawings (by others).

6. Driveway Stakes:
Including setting stakes at centerline of driveways by 4 ft offset to curbline

7. Individual Lot Corners:
Includes the setting of iron pins on all corners (or permanent marks in the sidewalk on the property lines extended where applicable) on each lot after fine grading is completed. State Law requires that all lot corners shall be marked unless we have written instructions from the "ultimate user", requesting that they not be set. The "ultimate user" is defined as the purchaser of the property or the attorney representing the purchaser. In the event that the developer does not wish to provide corner markers on all lots covered by this agreement, a statement must be signed by each "ultimate user" prior to the release of the final inspection survey for settlement and/or certificate of occupancy and forwarded to our office specifying that request corners, the developer will be charged $_____ / Lot which will be billed as an additional item in place of the per lot cost listed. The developer should allow for this additional cost to be included with any settlement costs.

All lot corners to be paid by Developer.
Individual lot corners as requested by "Ultimate User" to be paid by Developer.

Figure 5-7. Houseline Surveying Scope of Services.

HOUSELINE SURVEYING (Cont'd)

8. Individual Plot Plan:
   Including preparation of plan to a scale of 1in. - 30 ft.
   To be used as a base for building permit plan, foundation survey and final survey.

9. Individual Building Permit Plan:
   Including location of individual house on plan to be used for application for building permit. No house grades will be set.

10. House and Lot Grades:
    Including location of individual houses on lots, setting floor elevations and illustrating same on individual Plot Plans.

11. House Stakes:
    Including setting up of four stakes for line and grade to control individual house construction. This item will be applicable on wooded lots where lot clearing or house clearing stakes were previously completed. If lot is not cleared, billing will be on our normal time charge method of billing.

12. Foundation Location Survey:
    Including preparation of Title Survey Plan to a scale of 1in. = 50 ft illustrating location of existing house foundation.

13. Final Inspection Survey:
    Title Survey Plan to show complete house and type. Including a block and lot description typed on the plot plan. If a metes and bounds description is required, it will cost an additional $_____ / per lot. As-built lot grades are included as per Township requirements.

14. Pad Stakes:
    Including calculating location and setting four stakes for line and grade on building pad corners.

15. Re-Staking (for budget purposes only):   "TIME CHARGE"

16. Extra Work: "TIME CHARGE"
    Includes items of work requested but not included in the above contract. A proposal for said work will be submitted upon request.
    It is the Developer's responsibility to protect stakes once they are in place. Re-staking will be charged against item #15 and billed on our normal time method of billing.
    The Developer will be charged at actual cost for all prints supplied on the project.

    The above is proposed as a comprehensive list of professional surveying services commonly required on a specific development. Certain items may be deleted without affecting the other unit charges.
                    1 in. = 25 mm; 1 ft = 30 cm

Figure 5-7. Houseline Surveying Scope of Services—*continued.*

BOUNDARY SURVEY CHECKLIST

1. Caption giving property location (local, legal, land subdivision,municipality, County, State).

2. Point of Beginning.

3. Tie to established reference point.

4. Parcel Traversed in clockwise direction.

5. Type corner markers found and set indicated.

6. Courses shown in degrees, minutes, and seconds east or west of a north/south line.

7. Traverse closed.

8. Contiguous property owners indicated.

9. Name of streets, railroads, rivers, creeks, etc. shown.

10. Easements of record located.

11. Easements or Right-of-Way contiguous to or ending at boundary shown with ownership noted.

12. Location and dimensions adjacent road Rights-of-Ways.

13. Improvements located.

14. Encroachments located or noted, if none exist.

15. Flood plain note.

16. Curve data shown (points at curvature, tangency, and compound curvature; radii; central angle; and length and bearing of long chord).

17. Error of closure

18. Area (SF, if less than one acre and acres, if larger).

19. Metes and bounds description.

20. Easement descriptions.

21. Plat scale (1"= 50').

22. Date of survey and plat.

23. North Arrow (note whether true or magnetic).

24. Certification by surveyor.

    1 in.= 25 mm; 1 ft = 30 cm; 1 sq ft = 0.9 m²; 1 acre = 0.4 ha

Figure 7-1. Boundary Survey Checklist.

TOPOGRAPHIC SURVEY CHECKLIST

1. Boundary lines.
2. Topographic data, including 150' beyond property.
3. Letter of explanation, if permission to go on adjacent property not granted.
4. Location of structures, buildings, other man-made objects and important natural features.
5. Building floor elevation and other important elevations.
6. Location, size and type of materials for water lines, valves, meters, fire hydrants and other appurtenances servicing the property.
7. Location, size and type of materials for sanitary sewer lines servicing the property.
8. Sanitary sewer manholes with invert and top elevations
9. Direction of flow - sanitary sewer.
10. Location, size and type of materials for storm sewers and culverts servicing the property.
11. Catch basins and manholes located with invert and top elevations.
12. Storm flow direction for pipes, ditches, etc.
13. Location and size of gas lines servicing the property.
14. Electrical and telephone lines, including pole locations, servicing, located on or adjacent to the property.
15. Identity of utility owners and operators.
16. Outline perimeter of heavily wooded areas.
17. Location and site of solitary trees with 6 in. and larger diameter trunk.
18. Bench marks clearly described, one per four (4) acres with elevation given to 100th of foot.
19. Contour interval - one foot or as specified.
20. Elevations at high and low points.
21. Elevations at street intersections and every 50 ft along street at edges of pavement (both), curb and sidewalks.
22. Mean elevations and limits of standing or flowing water.
23. Limits of 100-year flood elevation or note, if 100-year flood does not encroach.
24. Identity of flood information source.
25. Location and ground elevation at all soil borings.
26. Caption showing location of property.
27. Map scale - 1"=50', or as specified.
28. North arrow.
29. Date of Survey.
30. Certification by surveyor.

     1 in. = 25 mm; 1 ft = 30 cm; 1 acre = 0.4 ha

Figure 7-2. Topographic Survey Checklist.

DECLARATION OF COVENANTS, CONDITIONS AND RESTRICTIONS

SECTION I - DEFINITIONS

1.1	By-Laws
1.2	Charges
1.3	Homeowners
1.4	Declarant
1.5	Dwelling Unit
1.6	Final Plan
1.7	Lot
1.8	Majority of Members
1.9	Member
1.10	Neighborhood
1.11	Owner
1.12	Parcel
1.13	Property
1.14	Residential Owner

SECTION II - APPLICABILITY

2.1	Applicability
2.2	Interpretation of Declaration

SECTION III - MEMBERSHIP

3.1	Membership
3.2	Termination of Membership
3.3	Voting Rights

SECTION IV - COVENANT FOR MAINTENANCE CHARGES

4.1	Creation of the Lien and Personal Obligations of Charges and Assessments
4.2	Owners' Negligence
4.3	Effect of Non-Payment of Charges and Assessments; Remedies of the Community Association
4.4	Lien of Charges
4.5	Annual Charges
4.6	Special Assessments

Figure 7-3. Declaration of Covenants, Conditions, and Restrictions.

SECTION V - ARCHITECTURAL REVIEW

5.1	Non-structural Improvements
5.2	Structural Improvements
5.3	Lot Improvements
5.4	Color Scheme Changes
5.5	Material Changes
5.6	Design Criteria and Standards
5.7	Plans and Specifications
5.8	Architectural Committee
5.9	Procedures
5.10	Waivers
5.11	Complaints and Appeals

SECTION VI - GENERAL PROVISIONS

6.1	Enforcement
6.2	Severability
6.3	Duration and Amendment
6.4	Dissolution

Figure 7-3. Declaration of Covenants, Conditions, and Restrictions—*continued.*

	Community Manager	Legal	Other	Date Start	Date Complete
HOMEOWNERS ASSOCIATION CHECKLIST **TURNOVER SCHEDULE**					
1. Date released for sale					
2. Documents recorded Copy received					
3. Anticipated closing of first units					
4. Set up Contracts					
A. Management					
B. Base contract and addendum approved					
C. Insurance					
D. Trash					
E. Lawn Maintenance					
F. Lease Agreement Approval					
G. Building Maintenance					
H. Pool Maintenance					
I. Apply for Tax I.D. #					
J. Others					
5. Deposits for:					
A. XYZ					
B. Utility					

Figure 7-4. Homeowners Association Checklist Turnover Schedule.

	Community Manager	Legal	Other	Date Start	Date Complete
6. Establish Bank Accounts Signature Cards					
A. Special Reserves 2 months					
B. Reserve - Monthly					
C. Operating - Operating Expense					
7. Set up Financial Records					
A. Accounts Receivables					
B. Accounts Payables					
8. Set up Files					
A. Alpha and numerical Files for owners					
B. Chronological file					
C. Miscellaneous Alpha File					
9. After Lease Agreement Approved					
A. Notify Real Estate Agent of Procedures					
B. Notify Owners					
10. Letter to Owners					
A. Notification of Assessment fee payment					
B. Set up coupon Payment book - printed					

Figure 7-4. Homeowners Association Checklist Turnover Schedule—*continued*.

	Community Manager	Legal	Other	Date Start	Date Complete
11. Set up rental package					
A. Welcome letter					
B. Include rules and Regulations					
12. Set up delinquent letter To be read					
13. Select and appoint Nominating & Transition Committee					
14. Solicit candidates for Board of Directors					
A. Send questionnaire to All owners					
B. Hold meeting to Determine candidates					
C. Establish election & Turnover date					
D. Notify all departments XYZ					
15. Mail election package Certified mail					
A. Notice of Meeting					
B. General Information					
C. Candidate's Resumes					
D. Ballot Information					
E. Ballot					
F. ID / Proxy					
G. Agenda					

Figure 7-4. Homeowners Association Checklist Turnover Schedule—*continued.*

	Community Manager	Legal	Other	Date Start	Date Complete
16. Preparation of Turnover Documents (per chpt 718)					
A. Declaration of Condominium & Amendments					
B. Articles of Incorporation					
C. Copy of By-Laws					
D. Minute book and Corporate Seal					
E. House rules & regs					
1. Resignation of officers - letters					
2. Financial records					
a. Preliminary Balance Sheet					
b. Advance & Delinquent Payments					
c. Tax Records					
d. Review of records by outside accountant					
F. Association Funds					
1. Bank Account Balances					
2 Checkbooks.					
G. Inventory of Personal Property					

Figure 7-4. Homeowners Association Checklist Turnover Schedule—*continued.*

	Community Manager	Legal	Other	Date Start	Date Complete
H. Plans&Specifications As Builts					
1. Roads					
2. Drainage					
3. Sprinkler system					
I. Insurance Policies					
J. Certificate of Occupancy					
K. Other permits - Swimming Pool					
L. Written Warranties					
M. Roster of Unit Owners					
N. Lease of Common Elements or Other Leases					
O. Employment Contract					
P. Service Contract					
Q. Deed for Common Property					
R. Affidavit of No Liens					
17. Establish transition period for turnover -- Directors-elect work with budget, contracts, rules etc.- with XYZ assistance for 30 days (under contract)					

Figure 7-4. Homeowners Association Checklist Turnover Schedule—*continued*.

	Community Manager	Legal	Other	Date Start	Date Complete
18. Conduct Election / Turnover Meeting					
A. Establish Quorum					
B. Call for Nomination From the Floor					
C. Call for All Ballots					
D. Count Ballots - Have Tally Sheets					
E. Announce Directors-Elect					
F. Acknowledge Form for Certification of Votes					
G. Present All Turnover Documents Listed Above					
H. Adjourn Meeting					

Figure 7-4. Homeowners Association Checklist Turnover Schedule—*continued.*

CONCEPTUAL COST ESTIMATE

Note: Adjust unit price consistent with the locale of the project.

PROJECT _____ LOT _____ BLOCK _____

Location _____

Concept Plan Date _____   By: _____

Number of Units _____   Date: _____

SUMMARY	PER UNIT CONCEPTUAL COST	COMMENT
Common Area:	_____	_____
Water System: On-Site	_____	_____
Off-Site	_____	_____
Sewer System: On-Site	_____	_____
Off-Site	_____	_____
Land Development: On-Site	_____	_____
Off-Site	_____	_____
Structure:	_____*_____	_____
Raw Land:	_____	_____
TOTAL HARD COSTS	_____	_____
TOTAL SOFT COSTS	_____	_____
Overhead	_____	_____
Per Unit Total Cost:	_____	_____
AVERAGE SALES PRICE	_____	_____

* FORMULAS PROVIDED

Figure 7-5. Conceptual Cost Estimate.

COST ANALYSIS

LOT _____ BLOCK _____   BY:_____
DATE: _____

DESCRIPTION OF WORK:	Conceptual Cost Per Unit	Comment
Site Feasibility	_____	_____
Survey Fees	_____	Houseline/Land Development
Site Planning and Design Development	_____	_____
Engineering Fees	_____	_____
Architect Fees	_____	$2000 - $5000 per model
Landscape Architect Fees	_____	_____
Civil Eng. Insp. & Certification Fees	_____	_____
Architectural Inspection Fees	_____	_____
Field Engineering & Survey Fees	_____	_____
Soil Testing	_____	_____
TOTAL PROFESSIONAL FEES	_____	
Regulatory Processing & Permit Fees	_____	Include all Agencies
Escrow & Regulatory Inspection Fees	_____	_____
Water Connection Fees	_____	_____
Sewer Connection Fees	_____	_____
Miscellaneous Fees	_____	_____
TOTAL REGULATORY FEES	_____	

*FORMULAS PROVIDED

Figure 7-5. Conceptual Cost Estimate—*continued.*

LOT _____ BLOCK _____   BY: _____

                              DATE: _____

                              Conceptual Cost

DESCRIPTION OF WORK: Per Unit   Comment

Planting Materials
  (Street Trees,Buffers,etc)   _____   _____

Sod / Seed   _____   Right of Way & Common Area

Irrigation System   _____   _____

Berms   _____   _____

Entry Feature   _____   _____

Perimeter Walls   _____   _____

TOTAL LANDSCAPING COSTS: _____

Project Utilities, Other   _____   _____

Cost for Electric Service   _____   _____

Entry Feature Lighting   _____   _____

Street Lights   _____   _____

Temporary Power   _____   _____

Amenity Lighting   _____   _____

Telephone Service   _____   _____

Cable T.V.   _____   _____

Mailboxes   _____   _____

Directories   _____   _____

Trash Enclosures   _____   _____

Wheel Stops   _____   _____

Amenities:

_____   _____   _____

_____   _____   _____

_____   _____   _____

Figure 7-5. Conceptual Cost Estimate—*continued.*

LOT _____ BLOCK _____   BY: _____

                              DATE: _____

                              Conceptual Cost
DESCRIPTION OF WORK: Per Unit   Comment

Water Distribution System: On-Site   *_____   _____

                           Off-Site   *_____   _____

Sewer Collection System: On-Site   *_____   _____

                           Off-Site   *_____   _____

OFFSITE LAND DEVELOPMENT

Clearing   *_____   _____

Grading   _____   _____

Soil Import / Export   _____   _____

Rock / Tree Removal   _____   _____

Defective Soil Removal   _____   _____

Storm Drainage (on site)   _____   _____

Structures (Bridges, culverts, etc.)   _____   _____

Roadways   _____   _____

Special Paving   _____   _____

Pavement Markings   _____   _____

Bike Paths / Street Sidewalks   _____   _____

Curb & Gutters   _____   _____

Traffic Signs & Traffic Control   _____   _____

Street Signs   _____   _____

Miscellaneous:_____   _____   _____

_____   _____   _____

TOTAL OFF-SITE LAND

DEVELOPMENT COSTS   _____

* FORMULAS PROVIDED

Figure 7-5. Conceptual Cost Estimate—*continued.*

LOT _____ BLOCK _____   BY: _____

DATE: _____

DESCRIPTION OF WORK:	Conceptual Cost Per Unit	Comment
ON-SITE LAND DEVELOPMENT		
Clearing	*	_____
Grading	*	_____
Soil Import / Export	*	_____
Rock Removal		_____
Defective Soil Removal		Use of Materials Onsite-Refer to Soils Report
Storm Drainage (off-site)	*	_____
Structures (Bridges, culverts, etc.)		_____
Roadways	*	_____
Special Pavement		For Marketing Purposes
Street Sidewalks	*	_____
Curbs & Gutters	*	_____
Traffic Signs / Street Signs	*	_____
Soil Erosion	*	_____
Driveway Aprons	*	_____
Street Trees	*	_____

TOTAL ON-SITE LAND
DEVELOPMENT COSTS   _____

**TOTAL LAND
DEVELOPMENT COSTS**   _____

COMMENTS: _____

_____

_____

* FORMULAS PROVIDED

Figure 7-5. Conceptual Cost Estimate—*continued.*

Formulas for Cost Analysis

Structure	Square Footage Cost x (sq ft + ½ Garage sq ft)
Water Distribution System	
On-Site:	(Total Length of Roads x Pipe Unit Price x 2)+ (No. Of Fire Hydrants x Unit Cost)
Off-Site	Same Formula as for Onsite
Sewer Collection System	
On-Site	(Total Length of Roads x Unit Price x 2) + (No. Of Manholes x Unit Cost)
Off-Site	Same Formula as for Onsite
Off-site Land Development	
Clearing	Width of Roadway to be Cleared x Unit Price x 1.3
On-Site Land Development	
Clearing	(Right of Way + 20 ft x Length of Roads x Unit Price) + (No. Of Lots x Unit Price per Lot)
Grading - Earthwork	Strip Topsoil - Total Area of Clearing x 1 ft x Unit Price General Grading-Total Area of Clearing (sq yds) x Unit Price Fill / Lot - (Per Lot Estimate of cu yd) x Unit Price Rough Grade - Total Area of Clearing x Unit Price Topsoil Replacement - Strip Topsoil Value x 0.4 Final Grade - Rough Grade Value x 0.4 (or $7000/acre)
Soil Import / Export	Truckload cu yds x 1.2 x Cost Per Truckload
Storm Drainage	1) Locate inlets at every low point and intersection No. Of Inlets x Unit Price 2) Locate inlets approx 250 - 300 ft from road highpoint (Use topo as guide) 3) Start with pipe length of 15 inches and increase diameter For pipe length downstream. Total Length x Unit Price
Roadways	Total Length of Roads x Width x Unit Price
Street Sidewalks	Width of Sidewalk x Length of Road x 2.2 x Unit Price
Curbs & Gutters	Length of Roadways x 2.2 x Unit Price
Traffic/Street Signs	No. Of Intersections x 6 x Unit Price
Soil Erosion	Linear Footage of Silt Fence x Unit Price No of Inlets x Unit Price
Driveway Aprons	No.of Lots x Unit Price
Street Trees	(Length of Roadways ÷ 50) x 2.2 x Unit Price

1 in.= 25 mm; 1 ft = 30 cm; 1 sq ft = 0.9 m^2; 1 sq yd = 0.8 m^2

Figure 7-5. Conceptual Cost Estimate—*continued.*

HOUSELINE BUDGET LINE ITEMS	
DESCRIPTION	
OCHD PERMIT FEE	
ZONING PERMIT	
TREE PERMIT	
FOUNDATION PERMIT	
BUILDING PERMIT FEE	
PRE-ENGINEERING FEE	
SEPTIC DESIGN & PLOT PLAN	
HL SURVEYING	
LOT CLEARING	
STRIP TOPSOIL	
FILL MATERIAL	
EXCAVATE BASEMENT	
EXTERMINATOR	
FOUNDATION	
BACKFILL BASEMENT	
LUMBER	
FRAMING	
ROOF TRUSSES	
EXTERIOR FRONT DOOR	
FYPON / COLUMNS	
WINDOW MATERIAL	
ROOFING	
SIDING	

Figure 7-6. Houseline Budget Line Items.

PLUMBING	
HVAC	
ELECTRIC	
GARAGE DOORS	
INSULATION	
SHEETROCK	
GUTTERS & LEADERS	
SHUTTERS	
INTERIOR STAIRS/ RAILS	
SEPTIC SYSTEM & TANK	
SEWER CONNECTION FEE	
WATER CONNECTION FEE	
WELL	
ROUGH GRADE/ DRIVE/ FLAT	
SERVICE WALKS & PATIOS	
DRIVEWAY PAVING	
INTERIOR TRIM MATERIAL	
INTERIOR TRIM LABOR	
WATER TEST	
SOFTENER	
CERAMIC TILE	
PAINTING	
CABINETS/TOPS	
CABS & TOPS INSTALL	
MIRROR & BATH ACCESS.	
VINYL FLOORING	
CLEANING ROUGH/ FINAL	
CARPETING	

Figure 7-6. Houseline Budget Line Items—*continued.*

HARDWARE	
RANGE/ HOOD/ DISHWASHER	
FINISH GRADE / RE-TOPSOIL	
PLANTINGS	
SEEDING	
FINAL ENGINEERING FEE	
WARRANTY INSURANCE	
CONSTRUCTION EXTRAS	
WARRANTY COMPANY	
200 - AMP SERVICE	
SECURITY SYSTEM	
FIREPLACE	

Figure 7-6. Houseline Budget Line Items—*continued.*

PROJECT PROFORMA

MARKET:
     Sales Price _____

     Number of Lots: _____

PER LOT ANALYSIS:

1. _____
   Land Purchase Price

2. _____
   Soft Costs i.e. design professionals, regulatory fees, application fees

3. _____
   Conceptual land development cost for "buildable" lots - use form

4. _____
   Offsite costs i.e. water, sewer, road improvements

5. _____
   Real Estate commission to sell new homes including advertising

6. _____
   Houseline costs including all lot costs for a finished lot

7. _____
   Interest and finance costs (land development and/or houseline)

8. _____
   Warranty services, Project turnover costs

9. _____
   Project overhead and General administrative

10. _____
    Subtotal   —

Figure 7-7. Project Pro Forma.

ENGINEERING PLAN REVIEW CHECKLIST

COVER SHEET CHECKLIST
( )   Project title and location.
( )   Location map with north arrow and scale.
( )   Project area identified on location map.
( )   Key map.
( )   Legend.
( )   Engineers notes, check for spelling and completeness.
( )   If notes are standard, make sure that the proper corrections have been made to
       make it applicable to project.
( )   Index of sheets

GENERAL
( )   Check notes for completeness and spelling
( )   Title blocks complete
( )   North arrow and scale
( )   Check with community subdivision regulations and engineering standards to make
       sure that all requirements are met.
( )   Proper cross reference is made between plan & detail sheets
( )   Grading and drainage has been coordinated with adjacent properties
( )   Adjacent properties identified
( )   Check with record plat to make sure that all right-of-ways & easement are shown
( )   Show block & lot numbers, also identify tracts, parks, waterways, street names
( )   Show all property dimensions
( )   Roadway and/or, driveway alignment is complete.
( )   Show bench marks if available
( )   Show all existing information
( )   Label existing information to remain, be removed, abandoned, etc.

PAVING & GRADING
( )   Show elevations at all inlets
( )   Existing topo is shown, including contours at one foot intervals
( )   Proposed grades are shown. Make sure that they are at or above flood criteria
( )   Check that vertical curves are shown when streetgrade has a difference of over 1%
( )   Show elevations at all low points, high points, break in grade, and intersections.
       Also show distance and slope between points.
( )   Roadways, driveways, bike paths, walkways are shown.
( )   Check that proper typical street section applies to road right-of-way,
( )   If applicable, check that proposed grade lines are properly shown.
( )   Check that finished floor elevation meet government requirements, building codes
       and yard drainage

DRAINAGE
( )   Primary drainage corresponds with drainage master plan of the area.

Figure 8-1. Engineering Plan Review Checklist.

( )   Direction of runoff is shown.
( )   All low points have provisions for drainage disposal.
( )   Label all pipes and show in pipe schedule (if one is used) the following:
    ( )   Pipe size.
    ( )   Pipe material.
    ( )   Length of pipe.
    ( )   Headwalls, if needed.
    ( )   Flow at peak if pipe schedule is used.
    ( )   Inverts, in and out.
( )   Check that pipe inverts and swale bottom elevations are coordinated.
( )   Check details for soakage pits, french drains, slab covered trenches, etc.
( )   Check for conflicts between drainage system and other utilities (water & sewer).
( )   Proper cover, provided on pipes.
( )   Identify type of inlets.
( )   Identify type of grates.

WATER DISTRIBUTION PLANS
( )   Check all notes for completeness and spelling.
( )   Title blocks complete.
( )   North arrow scale.
( )   Check with community subdivision regulations and engineering; standards to make
    sure that all requirements are met.
( )   Proper cross reference is made between plan and detail sheets.
( )   Show block and lot numbers, also identify tracts, parks, waterways, street names.
( )   Show all existing information.
    ( )   Existing water mains.
    ( )   Fire hydrants.
    ( )   Valves.
    ( )   Other utilities in area.
    ( )   Drainage structures.
    ( )   Buildings.
    ( )   Roadways.
( )   Check standard details to determine location of main with respect to r/w line.
( )   Label connections to existing water mains.
( )   If tapping, call out "wet tap and valve."
( )   Loop system if possible.
( )   Dead end lines should have blow-off valve at end.
( )   Show pipe size and material.
    ( )   Check regulations for minimum pipe size.
( )   Show valve locations.
( )   Show fire hydrants.
    ( )   Check regulations for maximum spacing.
    ( )   Minimum pipe size to fire hydrant to be six inches (6") diameter.
( )   Water service provided to all properties.
( )   Show all pipe fittings.
( )   Provide plug for pipes planned for future extensions.
( )   Check for conflicts.

Figure 8-1. Engineering Plan Review Checklist—*continued.*

( )   Vertical clearance.

( )   Horizontal clearance.

( ) Check for adequate cover over pipes

SEWAGE COLLECTION SYSTEM

( ) Check all notes for completeness and spelling.

( ) Title blocks complete.

( ) North arrow & scale.

( ) Check with community subdivision regulations and Engineering standards to make sure that all requirements are met.

( ) Proper cross reference is made between plan and detail sheets.

( ) Show block and lot numbers, also identify tracts, parks, waterways, street names

( ) Show all existing information.

    ( )   Existing sewer lines.

    ( )   Other utilities in area.

    ( )   Drainage structures.

    ( )   Buildings.

    ( )   Roadways.

( ) Show pipe size and material.

( ) Show length (center to center between manholes) and slope of sewer line.

( ) Show trench cuts.

( ) Show manhole and manhole number.

( ) Indicate top of manhole elevation.

( ) Indicate invert elevations of line at manhole.

( ) Show direction of flow.

( ) Locate (by stationing) all sewer laterals.

( ) Show location of sewer line with respect to right-of-way line.

( ) Show location of lift stations.

( ) Show location of treatment plant if possible.

( ) Show on plan view details of sewer and drainage system crossings.

( ) Indicate the minimum allowed cover.

DETAIL SHEET

( ) Complete title block.

( ) Check all standard details and complete by adding any particular information which may be needed.

( ) Detail titles and identifications are correct.

( ) Proper cross reference is provided between plan and detail sheet.

( ) Check general notes for completeness and spelling.

( ) Typical roadway and or driveway sections if different from community engineering standard.

( ) Pavement design.

    ( )   Surface course, type and thickness.

    ( )   Base course, type and thickness.

    ( )   Subbase stabilization.

Figure 8-1. Engineering Plan Review Checklist—*continued.*

( )   Pavement slopes.
( )   Pavement width.
( )   Sidewalks.
( )   Curbs and gutters.
( )   Swales.
( )   Property lines.
( )   All features properly dimensioned.
( )   Typical grading details if used.
        ( )   Lot grading.
        ( )   Cul-de-sac grading.
        ( )   Green areas.
        ( )   Block grading.
( )   Show section for waterway, lake, ditch, retention basin, etc.
        ( )   Maximum side slopes.
        ( )   Grading up to the property line.
        ( )   Right-of-ways.
( )   Detail all drainage structures and systems which are not part of community engineering standards.
        ( )   Inlets.
        ( )   Grates.
        ( )   French drains.
        ( )   Soakage pit.
        ( )   Slab covered trench.
        ( )   Control structures (weirs, culverts, etc.).
( )   Check headwall size required and make sure that the area around the structure has been graded properly.
( )   Provide details of erosion protection systems if required.
( )   Protective slab detail for pipes with less than minimum cover.

WATER SYSTEM
( )   Thrust block details.
( )   Typical meter-service assembly.
( )   Blow off valve detail.
( )   Gate value and box detail.
( )   Wet tap and valve detail.
( )   Sampling point details.
( )   Typical pipe, valve and hydrant location detail.
( )   Typical hydrant and valve detail.
( )   Special crossing details.
( )   Protective slab and anchoring for pipes with less than minimum cover.
( )   Detail water and sewer crossing if less than minimum clearance is provided (Vertical. 18 inches and/or Horizontal: 10 ft).
( )   Trench backfill detail.
( )   Pavement restoration detail

Figure 8-1. Engineering Plan Review Checklist—*continued*.

SEWAGE SYSTEM
( )   Standard lift station detail sheet.
      ( )   Location map.
      ( )   Typical wet well installation.
      ( )   Wet well sections.
      ( )   Wet well plan view.
      ( )   Wet well notes.
      ( )   Pump data.
      ( )   Electrical notes.
      ( )   Electrical diagram.
      ( )   Force main data.
      ( )   Bill of materials.
( )   Brick manhole.
( )   Precast manhole.
( )   Manhole frame and cover.
( )   Standard drop connections.
( )   Sewer riser detail.
( )   Sewer lateral detail.
( )   Terminal clean out detail.
( )   Protective slab detail for pipes with less than minimum cover.
( )   Trench width details.
( )   Trench backfill details.
( )   Bedding details.
( )   Pavement details.
( )   Air release valve.
( )   Detail water and sewer crossing if less than minimum clearance is provided (vertical 18 inches and or horizontal 10-ft).
( )   Show fire hydrants.
      ( )   Check regulations for maximum spacing.
      ( )   Minimum pipe size to fire hydrant to be six inches (6") diameter.
( )   Water service provided to all properties.
( )   Show all pipe fittings.
( )   Provide plug for pipes planned for future extensions.
( )   Check for conflicts.
      ( )   Vertical clearance.
      ( )   Horizontal clearance.
( )   Check for adequate cover on pipes.

1 in. = 25 mm; 1 ft = 30 cm

Figure 8-1. Engineering Plan Review Checklist—*continued.*

PROFORMA LAND DEVELOPMENT BUDGET			# of Units	
PROJECT :				
ITEM	PRELIM DATE	REVISED DATE	BID DATE	BUDGET DATE
SURVEYING				
Boundary & Topo Survey				
Roadways and Sitework				
Curbs and Gutters				
Building Pad Layout				
Sanitary Sewer Layout				
Force Main Layout				
Water Main Layout				
Drainage Layout				
Sidewalk Layout				
As Builts				
Clearing				
Restaking				
Other Surveying				
TOTAL SURVEYING				
ENGINEERING				
Design On-site & Off-site				
Plat Preparation				
Record Plat				
Testing				
Inspection & Certifications				
Drafting				
Printing Charges				
Quantity Takeoffs				
Other Engineering				
TOTAL ENGINEERING				

Figure 8-2. Pro Forma Land Development Budget.

PROJECT	PRELIM	REVISED	BID	BUDGET
	DATE	DATE	DATE	DATE
DEVELOPMENT FEES				
Permits & Submission Fees				
School Fees				
Park Dedication				
Other Impact Fees				
Electric Fees				
Water Connection Fees				
Sewer Connection Fees				
Cable TV				
Telephone				
Inspection Fees				
Construction Bonds				
Escrows				
Other Fees				
TOTAL DEVELOPMENT FEES				
MOBILIZATION				
Trailer Delivery & Setup				
Electric Deposit & Hookup				
Telephone Deposit & Hookup				
Water and Sewer				
Temporary Road & Parking Area				
Barricades				
Landscaping				
Interior Improvements				
Exterior Improvements				
Signage & Barricades				
Permits				
TOTAL MOBILIZATION				

Figure 8-2. Pro Forma Land Development Budget—*continued*.

PROJECT	PRELIM	REVISED	BID	BUDGET
	DATE	DATE	DATE	DATE
SITEWORK				
Clearing and Grubbing				
Grassing and Mulching				
Tree Removal				
Trash Removal				
Rock Removal				
Lake Excavation				
Strip Topsoil				
Rough Grade (Cut & Fill Balance)				
Finish Building Pads				
Hauling Material Off-site				
Import Fill Material				
Demucking				
Testing				
Other Sitework				
TOTAL SITEWORK				
STORM DRAINAGE				
Pipework				
Headwalls, Flared End Sections				
Inlets, Manholes				
Outlet Structures				
Rip Rap				
Other				
TOTAL STORM DRAINAGE				

Figure 8-2. Pro Forma Land Development Budget—*continued.*

PROJECT :	PRELIM DATE	REVISED DATE	BID DATE	BUDGET DATE
SANITARY SEWER				
Pipework				
Manholes				
Force Main				
Lift Station				
Service Connections				
Connection to Existing Line				
Testing				
Other				
TOTAL SANITARY SEWER				
WATER DISTRIBUTION				
Pipework				
Valves, T's, Crosses, etc.				
Fire Hydrants				
House Connections				
Connect to Existing Line				
Testing				
Other				
TOTAL WATER DISTRIBUTION				
TEMPORARY UTILITIES				
Electric				
Water				
Sewer				
Other				
TOTAL TEMPORARY UTILITIES				

Figure 8-2. Pro Forma Land Development Budget—*continued.*

PROJECT :	PRELIM	REVISED	BID	BUDGET
	DATE	DATE	DATE	DATE
PAVING				
Cut Roads				
Grade, Spread & Compact				
Stabilized Subgrade				
Asphalt Base				
Asphalt Surface Course				
Resurfacing				
Leveling Course				
Milling Operations				
Signs and Stripping				
Curb and Gutter				
Stone				
Other				
TOTAL PAVING				
LOT PREPARATION				
Lot Clearing				
Remove Unsuitable Material				
Deliver Fill to Lot				
Cut & Fill Operations				
Pad Construction				
Flatwork Grading				
Final Grade				
Driveway				
Driveway Apron				
Repair Road at Connection				
Other				
TOTAL LOT PREPARATION				

Figure 8-2. Pro Forma Land Development Budget—*continued.*

PROJECT :	PRELIM	REVISED	BID	BUDGET
	DATE	DATE	DATE	DATE
R/W & COMMON AREAS				
Street Trees				
Entry Feature landscaping				
Entry Features, Walls, Fences				
Sidewalks				
Irrigation System				
Other				
TOTAL R/W & COMMON AREAS				
FINAL SURVEYING				
Plot Plan				
Clearing Limits				
Grade Stakes				
Building Stakeout				
Foundation Location Plan				
Final Survey				
Monuments				
Other				
TOTAL FINAL SURVEYING				
SUBTOTAL DEVELOPMENT COST				
LAND DEVELOPMENT CONTINGENCY				
OVERHEAD				
PROPERTY TAXES				
INTEREST				
MISCELLANEOUS				
TOTAL COST				
TOTAL COST PER UNIT				

Figure 8-2. Pro Forma Land Development Budget—*continued.*

RESIDENTIAL LAND DEVELOPMENT SPECIFICATIONS OUTLINE

1. DEFINITIONS OF TERMS

1.1	General
1.2	Act of God
1.3	Addendum
1.4	Bidder
1.5	Change Order
1.6	Contract
1.7	Contra at Documents
1.8	Subcontractor
1.9	Directed, Ordered, Approval and etc.
1.10	Engineer
1.11	General Conditions and Specifications
1.12	Inspector
1.13	Laboratory
1.14	Owner
1.15	Performance and payment boards
1.16	Plans
1.17	Proposal
1.18	Proposal Guarantee
1.19	Special Conditions
1.20	Specifications
1.21	Supplemental Agreement
1.22	Surety
1.23	Written Notice
1.24	A.S.T.M Designation

2. PLANS, SPECIFICATIONS AND RELATED DATA

2.1	Intent of Plans and Specifications
2.2	Conflict
2.3	Discrepancies in Plans
2.4	Drawing and Specifications at Sub Site
2.5	Dimensions
2.6	Sampling and Testing
2.7	Shop Drawings
2.8	Quality of Equipment and Materials
2.9	Equipment Approval Data

3. ENGINEER, OWNER, SUBCONTRACTOR RELATIONS

3.1	Engineer's Responsibility and Authentity
3.2	Engineer's Decisions

Figure 12-1. Residential Land Development Specifications Outline.

3.3	Suspension of Work
3.4	Extension of Time for Suspension
3.5	Construction Review of Work
3.6	Field Tests and Preliminary Operation
3.7	Examination of Completed Work
3.8	Subcontractor's Superintendent
3.9	Private Property
3.10	Assignment of Contract
3.11	Owners Right to Correct Deficiencies
3.12	Owners Right to Terminate Contract and Complete Work
3.13	Subcontractor's Right to Suspend Work
3.14	Rights of Various Interests
3.15	Separate Contracts
3.16	Subcontracts and Purchase Orders
3.17	Work Drawing an Emergency
3.18	Oral Agreements
3.19	Night and Sunday Work
3.20	Hold Harmless Clause
3.21	Unauthorized Work
3.22	Use of Completed Portions of the Work
3.23	Subcontractors Responsibility for Work

4. MATERIALS AND WORKMANSHIP

4.1	Materials Furnished by the Subcontractor
4.2	Storage of Materials
4.3	Character of Workmen
4.4	Rejected Work and Materials
4.5	Manufacturer's Direction
4.6	Cutting and Patching
4.7	Cleaning Up
4.8	Ownership of Materials
4.9	Guarantee

5. INSURANCE, LEGAL RESPONSIBILITY AND PUBLIC SAFETY

5.1	Insurance
5.2	Indemnity
5.3	Board
5.4	Patents and Royalties
5.5	Permits
5.6	Laws to be Observed
5.7	Protection of Persons and Property
5.8	Crossing Utilities
5.9	Sanitary Provisions
5.10	Warning Signs and Barricades

Figure 12-1. Residential Land Development Specifications Outline—*continued.*

5.11	Field Offices

6. PROGRESS AND COMPLETION OF WORK

6.1	Notice to Proceed
6.2	Contract Time
6.3	Schedule of Completion
6.4	Coordination of Construction
6.5	Protection of Existing Utilities and Facilities
6.6	Changes in the Work
6.7	Extension of Contract Time
6.8	Liquidated Damages for Failure to Complete Work

7. CONSTRUCTION SPECIFICATIONS

7.1	Surveying
7.2	Clearing
7.3	Soil Erosion
7.4	Excavation
7.5	Storm Drains
7.6	Sanitary Sewer / Water Distribution
7.7	Curbs and Gutters
7.8	Sidewalks
7.9	Asphalt Paving / Roadways and Driveways
7.10	Landscaping

8. MEASUREMENT AND PAYMENT

8.1	Detailed Breakdown of Contract Amount
8.2	Request for Payment
8.3	Engineer's Action on a Request for payment
8.4	Owner's Action on a Request for payment
8.5	Owner's Right to Withhold Payment of a Request for Payment
8.6	Payment for Uncorrected Work
8.7	Payment for Rejected Work and Materials
8.8	Changes in the Work
8.9	Canceled Items of Work
8.10	Payment for Work Suspended by the Owner
8.11	Payment for Work by the Owner
8.12	Payment for Work by the Owner following termination of Contract
8.13	Payment for Work Suspended by the Subcontractor
8.14	Release of Liens (Interim/ Final)
8.15	Acceptance and Final Payment
8.16	Termination of Subcontractor's Responsibility
8.17	Satisfaction of Warranty Work After Final Payment

Figure 12-1. Residential Land Development Specifications Outline—*continued.*

9. INFORMATION FOR BIDDERS
        9.1   Conditions of Work
        9.2   Qualifications of Bidders
        9.3   Preparation of Bids
        9.4   Bid Security
        9.5   Receipt and opening of Bids
        9.6   Analysis of Bid Prices
        9.7   Right to Accept and Reject Bids
        9.8   Acceptance of Bid and Award of Contract
        9.9   Security for Faithful Performance
        9.10   Time of Completion
        9.11   Substitution of Equipment and/or Material

Figure 12-1. Residential Land Development Specifications Outline—*continued.*

SUMMARY
LAND DEVELOPMENT CONTRACT PROCEDURE

Prebid Conference With Operational Staff

- Review project specifics
- Outline construction needs, schedule
- Highlight contractor recommendations
- Define time tables

Bid Process

- Schedule prebid meeting with contractors
- Distribute plans to contractors
- Schedule contractor meetings as necessary
- Prepare spread sheets, analyze schedule of values against cost estimate
- Resolve discrepancies
- Ensure contractors understand scope of work
- Prepare scope of work, spread sheets, and recommendations

CONTRACTS

- Complete final negotiations
- Select contractor
- Type, process, and execute contract

PRE-CONSTRUCTION MEETING

- Meet with field representative, design engineer, contractors, utility companies, architect, and government officials prior to construction start.

Figure 12-2. Summary Land Development Contract Procedure.

CONTRACTOR INFORMATION SHEET

NAME_____ DATE _____

BUSINESS ADDRESS_____ PHONE _____

RESIDENCE ADDRESS_____ PHONE _____

CONTRACTOR LICENSE # _____ OCCUPATIONAL LICENSE #_____

FEDERAL TAX ID _____ NUMBER OF EMPLOYEES _____

TYPE OF BUSINESS: PARTNERSHIP, CORPORATION, SELF-EMPLOYED, OTHER:___

INSURANCE: <u>AMOUNT</u>

      GENERAL LIABILITY INSURANCE   _____

      AUTO INSURANCE   _____

      WORKMEN'S COMPENSATION   YES_____NO_____

GENERAL DESCRIPTION OF COMPANY ASSETS / EQUIPMENT:

_____

_____

_____

_____

HAVE YOU WORKED FOR _____ BEFORE? YES _____ NO _____

WHEN _____ WHERE _____

TYPE OF WORK YOU ARE BIDDING ON _____

_____

REFERENCES:

            NAME   ADDRESS   PHONE

BANK #1 _____

BANK #2 _____

SUPPLIER #1_____

SUPPLIER #2 _____

CUSTOMER #1 _____

CUSTOMER #2 _____

PREVIOUS YEARS SALES VOLUME $_____

Figure 12-3. Contractor Information Sheet.

BID ANALYSIS EXAMPLE

		ABC Construction		Able Builders	
	Description	Unit Price	Total	Unit Price	Total
1.	Mobilization		$28,000.00		$37,700.00
2.	Clearing	37.6@$1000	37,600.00	36@$675	24,300.00
3.	Retention Area	43,966@$1.88	82,656.08	43,706@$1.73	75,611.38
4.	Road Grading	21,927@$.76	16,664.52	21,980@$1.55	34,069.00
5.	6" Comp.Sub-Base	21,927@$.50	10,968.50	24,920@$.53	12,873.70
6.	6" Limerock Base	20,500@$5.67	116,235.00	21,980@$6.15	135,177.00
7.	Prime	19,525@$.19	3,709.75	21,980@$.25	5,495.00
8.	1"Type II Asphalt(S-1)	19,525@$1.93	37,083.25	21,980@$1.97	43,399.60
9.	Type "A" Curb	1,743@$4.95	8,627.85	2,430@$4.70	11,421.00
10.	Valley Gutter	10,575@$4.68	49,491.00	10,397@$5.25	54,584.25
11.	Stabilized Soil	1,011@$6.59	6,662.49	3220@$5.40	7,388.00
12.	Street Signs	14@$103.50	1,449.00	16@$75	1,200.00
13.	Stop Signs	6 @$92	552.00	16@$90	1,440.00
14.	Lot Prep	182@$693.81	126,273.42	183@$275	50,325.00
15.	Seed,Mulch,Fert.	58,253@$.30	17,475.90	40,000@$.12	4,800.00
16.	Fill Ditch	4901@$.75	3,676.75	move stockpile	-----
	Subtotal -Interior		$547,719.51		$509.684.93

Figure 12-4. Bid Analysis Example.

RECTIFIED BIDS***

	Quantity	Unit Price	Total	Budget Est.
Mobilization			24,000	30,000
Clearing	36.8	838	30,838	52,750
Detention	45,283	1.74	78,792	68,000
Rd Grading	21,954	1.16	25,467	27,000
Subbase	23,066	0.50	11,533---	
Base	21,133	5.65	119,401	
Prime	21,133	0.21	4,438	--------175,540
Type II	21,133	1.98	41,843---	
Type A Curb	1,988	4.83	9,602---	
Valley	10,608	4.97	52,722--- ------	69,600
Stab. Soil	1,216	6.17	7,503	6,000
Street Signs	16	115.00	1,840	2,835
Stop Signs	15	98.00	1,470	
Lot Prep	182	477.00	86,814	57,750
Seed/Mulch	37,988	.21	7,977	15,022
Fill Ditch			1,838	

*** High & Low Bid Cancel & Avg of 2 remaining Bids _____
     If all 4 Bid Line Items were close then an average
     was used - represents cost of project. $506,078 $504,397

```
                    Storm Drainage
                         135,381-----------------------------------
                         141,562
                         150,190-----------------------------------------------
                         178,432
                         178,533


13,129          -------RECTIFIED        641,459
=2%       ---- |                        654,587   +50,000 Surveying
              |                                   + 7,500 Bond    =$712,087
              -----
=16%      |-- NEGOTIATED BID            551,051
```

NOTE: Rectified   Design Additions
          641,459   +   11,995   = $653,454
                                                                      $4597
          551,051   +   107,000   = $658,051
                                   Fill
                                 47,000
                                 13,000
                                 47,000

Figure 12-4. Bid Analysis Example—*continued*.

LAND DEVELOPMENT CONTRACT PROVISIONS

1. Description and Scope of Work
2. Specifications
3. Plans and Miscellaneous Details
4. Time of Completion
5. Work Schedules
6. Compensation and Payment Schedule
7. Extra Work
8. Inspections
9. Work by Others
10. Existing Utilities
11. Testing
12. Precedence
13. General Conditions
14. Contractor Knowledge of Site
15. Payment and Performance Bond
16. Shop Drawings
17. Subcontractors
18. Construction Staking
19. Special Conditions

Figure 12-5. Land Development Contract Provisions.

LAND DEVELOPMENT CONTRACT EXAMPLE

FORMING PART OF CONTRACT   EFFECTIVE DATE:

CONTRACTOR: DATE:
SUBCONTRACT NO:
ADDENDUM NO:
SUB-CONTRACTOR: SUB-CONTRACTOR PHONE:
INDIVIDUAL (CONTACT):
FOR WORK AT:
CATEGORY OF WORK:

1. DESCRIPTION AND SCOPE OF WORK

 This Sub-Contractor shall provide all labor, material, equipment and supervision necessary to complete all clearing, soil erosion devices, excavation, grading, drainage, water, sewer, and paving as required to construct the project known as the plans and specifications prepared by   in accordance with   entitled

2. SPECIFICATIONS

 All work shall be performed in accordance with the following specification documents:

3. PLANS AND MISCELLANEOUS DETAILS

 All work shall be performed as per Plans and Details by   as listed below:

SHEET NO.	TITLE / DESCRIPTION	DATE

4. TIME OF COMPLETION

 The Sub-Contractor shall commence work within ten (10) days after written notice to proceed and attendance of a preconstruction meeting scheduled by the Contractor.

Figure 12-6. Land Development Contract Example.

5. WORK SCHEDULES

The Sub-Contractor shall abide by and shall perform all construction tasks in a timely manner in order to complete all work within the framework of the work schedule previously submitted to and approved by the Contractor.

6. COMPENSATION

a. This contract is a lump sum contract for total lump sum amount of $

b. Seeding, as required, shall be on a unit price basis of $ per acre, not to exceed acres. Billing to be based on as-built field measurements verified by the contractors representatives.

c. Final payment will be made to the Sub-Contractor within thirty (30) days of satisfactory completion of the project and acceptance by the Contractor. Final payment will not be made until all punch lists and deficiencies are corrected and approved by all government jurisdictions and the Contractor.

7. EXTRA WORK

It is understood and agreed that the Sub-Contractor shall not perform any additional work under this agreement for which the Contractor is to be invoiced without written authorization in the form of an executed Change Order to this agreement.

8. INSPECTION

All work performed under this agreement will be inspected by representatives of the contractor. The Sub-Contractor should also anticipate that the work performed under this contract will be inspected by appropriate Governmental Authorities, Engineers, Architects and Utility Companies.

Should any part of the sub-work, upon inspection, be found to be deficient and thus rejected, the Sub-Contractor shall correct all deficiencies within seven (7) days of written notice and immediately request a reinspection.

9. WORK BY OTHERS

The Sub-Contractor shall coordinate his work with the appropriate Utility Companies, i.e. electrical power, telephone, cable television, water and sewer in the installation of their facilities.

10. EXISTING SCHEDULES

The Sub-Contractor shall be responsible for obtaining all existing utility locations to avoid conflicts/damage to those facilities Damages and any costs associated with the repair of existing utilities shall be borne by the Sub-Contractor.

Figure 12-6. Land Development Contract Example—*continued.*

11. TESTING

The Contractor will provide all engineering testing by an independent soils testing laboratory. The results of all tests performed by said testing laboratory will be the final authority in the determination and verification that work performed by the Sub-Contractor is in compliance with all specified criterion. The Sub-Contractor shall be responsible for the costs of any re-testing should the initial tests fail. Tests will be scheduled by the contractor coordinated with the sub-contractors requests.

In addition, the Sub-Contractor shall be responsible for all testing and acceptance of water and sewer lines as required by the Municipal Utilities Authority. The cost of utilities testing including waterline disinfection performed by the Sub-Contractor is included within the total lump sum amount of this contract.

12. PRECEDENCE

Should there be any discrepancies between the Plans, Standard Specifications, the Sub-contractor's Bid Proposal, other Contract Documents and the Agreement, the Terms and Conditions of the Agreement shall prevail.

13. GENERAL

a.   The Sub-Contractor shall abide by all Governmental codes and ordinances required by Federal, State and Local Agencies.
b.   The Sub-Contractor shall be duly licensed by all agencies concerned to perform the workscope:
c.   All temporary water, sanitary and electrical facilities required shall be the responsibility of the Sub-Contractor,
d.   All work performed by the Sub-Contractor is warranted for one (1) year from the date of completion.
e.   Retainer: In the event the Contractor deems it necessary to replace the Sub-Contractors or suppliers due to any aforementioned factors, the Contractor, reserves the right to retain the balance of any monies owed for any and all work to sub-contractor at the time of their dismissal, for a period to be determined by the contractor, in order to appropriate the completion of works, faulty workmanship, and service work to the satisfaction of the Sub-Contractor.
f.   Progress Schedule: It shall be this Sub-Contractor's or suppliers responsibility to obtain and maintain a progress schedule and to accelerate same as required upon notice from the Contractor. Any delay caused by this Sub-Contractor or supplier not rectified within twenty-four (24) hours after having received written or verbal notice, shall constitute a breach of this agreement, shall allow the Contractor to exercise his legal rights under the terms and conditions of this subcontract agreement.

Figure 12-6. Land Development Contract Example—*continued.*

g. The Sub-Contractor shall employ a competent Superintendent and/or any necessary assistants who shall be on the project site full time during the progress of all work. The Superintendent shall represent the Sub-Contractor and all communications given to the Superintendent shall be as binding as if given to the sub-Contractor.

h. The Sub-Contractor shall adhere to all OSHA requirements.

i. The Sub-Contractor shall remove all rubbish, trash and debris accumulated in connection with his work on a continuing basis as work progresses. Trees, brush and all other vegetation accumulated as a result of land clearing shall be removed from the jobsite to a disposal area provided by the Sub-Contractor. The cost of debris removed by the Sub-Contractor is included in the lump sum.

14. CONTRACTOR KNOWLEDGE OF SITE

The Sub-Contractor agrees that he has thoroughly investigated the site and completed all quantification and costs to complete all construction of the project per plans and specifications within the lump sum price.

15. SHOP DRAWINGS

The Sub-Contractor shall submit seven (7) copies of all Shop Drawings as necessary to the Engineer/Architect for approval. Shop Drawings shall be submitted with reasonable promptness and in orderly sequence so As to cause no delay in the work. The Sub-Contractor shall make any corrections required by the Engineer/Architect and shall re-submit the required number of corrected copies until approved. No portion of the work requiring a Shop Drawing submission shall commence until the submission has been approved by the Engineer/Architect. Should the Sub-Contractor proceed with work without approved Shop Drawings he does so at his own risk.

16. PAYMENT AND PERFORMANCE BOND

The contractor shall furnish the contractor with a Payment and Performance Bond at least equal to the contract amount as security for the faithful payment and performance of all contractors obligations under the contract documents. The bond shall be furnished to the contractor prior to the commencement of work otherwise this agreement will not be executed. If the subcontractor is unable to produce the required bonding, this agreement shall be null and void.

17. SUB-CONTRACTORS

The Contractor reserves the right to at any time reject any Sub-Contractor or Organization including Material Suppliers. The Sub-Contractor shall not sub-contract any work outlined in this agreement without prior approval by the Contractor. This list of Sub-Contractors provided to the Contractor by the Sub-Contractor, prior to the execution of this Agreement shall govern unless a request for a change is submitted in writing and approved in writing by the Contractor.

Figure 12-6. Land Development Contract Example—*continued.*

18. SURVEY AND STAKING

The Contractor will furnish all construction staking and obtain all as-built information as required. Construction staking furnished by the Contractor will be one-time only. The Sub-Contractor shall take due care during construction so as not to destroy any staking furnished by the Contractor. Any re-staking performed by the Contractor required due to negligence by the Sub-Contractor shall be at the Sub-Contractor's expense.

19. SPECIAL CONDITIONS

a. The Sub-Contractor acknowledges that he has received, reviewed and understands the permits issued. These permits are contained in the attached composite "Exhibit A" to this agreement and are hereby incorporated by reference. The Sub-Contractor agrees to adhere to all conditions relative to the Sub-Contractors work which are set forth in the permits. In the event here is an alleged violation of the permits which relate to the work being conducted by the Sub-Contractor, the Sub-Contractor agrees to defend and indemnify the contractor against such alleged violation. In the event any fees, fines or penalties are imposed upon the Contractor, as a result of such violation, Sub-contractor agrees to pay said fees, fines or penalties imposed by the Governmental Agency. Furthermore, if the Contractor sustains any other losses as the result of such violation(s), Sub-Contractor agrees to compensate the Contractor for such losses.

b. All stumps and debris shall be carted off the jobsite to a licensed landfill or dumpslte. Burying of stumps and debris is prohibited.

c. Any damage done by subcontractors personnel shall be repaired and/or replaced at the sole expense of the Sub-Contractor. If repaired by the Contractor, the cost shall be back charged to the Sub-Contractor,

d. Sub-contractor shall protect his work at all times and shall be solely responsible for any damage done to his work and repairs needed to his work.

e. Any additional fees or costs created by Sub-Contractor due to failure of, or re-scheduling of inspections is the sole responsibility of this Sub-Contractor.

f. Street and parking subgrade and building pads within fill areas will be compacted to 95% of standard proctor.

g. Pad to be minimum five (5) feet over building line and within (+) 0.17 feet of pad grade.

h. All imported fill to be acceptable structural material of uniform quality.

i. Corrections of mistakes in the work performed by the Sub-Contractor shall begin immediately during normal working hours. Failure to complete these items will be sufficient cause to withhold draw.

j. All invoices are to be submitted to and approved by job Superintendent. Payment will be for completed work only. Any pay requests received in the Corporate office will be sent to the job site trailer and will result in delayed payment.

k. Water and sewer laterals shall be installed two (2) feet minimum behind the curbline including a capped cleanout.

Figure 12-6. Land Development Contract Example—*continued*.

l. Curb and gutter areas will be compacted to 95% of standard proctor.

m. Sub-Contractor to guarantee concrete to have a minimum 28 d compressive strength of 3,500 psi.

n. Sub-Contractor is to exercise care in grading, dumping, rolling, etc., near fences, trees, buildings, curb and gutter. Should damage result to any of the above mentioned items, it is the responsibility of the Sub-contractor to pay for the damages.

o. Sub-Contractor to broom clean stabilized base and apply tack coat prior to application of top coat.

p. This Sub-Contractor is responsible for all pavement restoration of existing paved roadways which are disturbed by his work.

q. Landscaping, lighting and the final pavement overlay of Melody Lane are not included in this contract.

r. This Sub-Contractor shall be responsible to control on-site drainage so as to ensure access to all building construction areas.

s. This Sub-Contractor shall be responsible to restore the off-site sanitary sewer easement and affected areas back to the existing condition of the easement.

t. This Sub-Contractor shall be conscious of any wetlands present on the site and/or delineated on the site plans. Sub-Contractor shall be held responsible for any disturbance of wetlands incurred as a result of his work. In the event any fines or penalties are imposed upon the contractor, as the result of such violation, Sub-Contractor agrees to pay said fees, fines or penalties imposed by the Governmental agency. Furthermore, if the contractor sustains any other losses as the result of such violation(s), Sub-Contractor agrees to compensate the contractor for such losses.

u. Prior to the installation of sanitary sewer facilities the construction permit must be issued by the State. The sub-contractor as a part of this contract must comply with the provisions of the construction permit issued for this project.

1 ft = 30 cm; 1 acre = 0.4 ha

Figure 12-6. Land Development Contract Example—*continued.*

LAND DEVELOPMENT
BUDGET VS. BID REPORT

Project Name:
Date:
Prepared By:
Reviewed By: Distribution: Field Office

Description	Budget Date: By:	Contract Amount Date: By:	Variance	Contractor
Storm Drainage	$ 86,000.00	$83,270.00	$2,730.00	XYZ Co.
Sanitary Sewer	$ 18,000.00	$19,900.00	($1,900.00)	XYZ Co.
Surveying	$ 10,000.00			
Electric Service	$ 10,000.00			
Road Paving	$ 35,000.00			
Soil Erosion	$ 7,500.00			
Excavation	$ 15,000.00			
Street Signs	$ 1,000.00			
Street Trees	$ 1,000.00			
Curb & Gutter	$ 5,000.00			
Water Distribution	$ 20,000.00			
Clearing	$ 22,000.00			
Sidewalks	$ 1,000.00			
Other	$ 16,000.00			
Subtotal	$247,500.00			
10% Contingency	$ 24,750.00			
TOTAL	$272,250.00			

Figure 12-7. Land Development Budget Versus Bid Report.

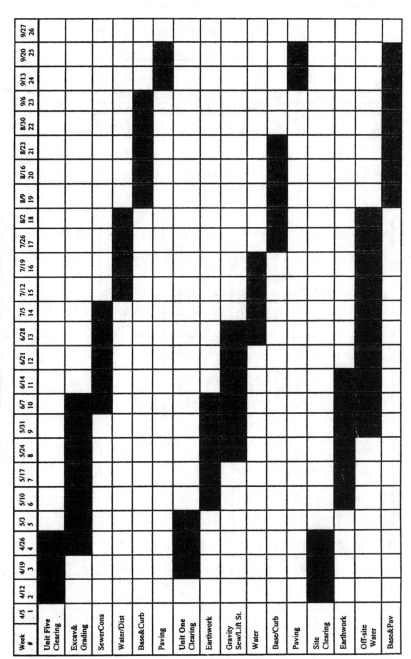

Figure 13-1. Land Development Progress Schedule.

SCHEDULE OF VALUES ANALYSIS

Project :_____ By:_____
Location:_____ Date:_____

CONTRACT		INVOICE PERIODS			
% Complete	Contract	3/15-5/15	5/15-7/15	7/15-8/15	8/15-9/15
	Addendum 1	$973,682			
15%	Invoice 1	$142,593	$831,089		
22%	Invoice 2		$66,868	$764,221	
24%	Invoice 3		$24,662	$739,559	
	Change Order1		$83,820		
50%	Invoice 1			$41,910	$41,910
				$0	$41,910
	15-Jul Work Order 00908			$2,040	
	Construct Pad Sequence 312			$2,040	$0
% Work Completed	Activity	Invoice 1 3/15-5/15	Invoice 2 5/15-7/15	Invoice 3 7/17-8/15	8/15-9/15
100% $13,986	*Clearing* 12.6 acres @	$10,000	$3,986		
		$3,986	$0		
50%	*Rough Grading* 5,730 cy @ $8595	$3,255	$5,340		
75%		$1,245	$4,095		
50%	*12" Stabil. Subgrade* 9,517 sy @ $16,180			$6,180	$10,000

1 in. = 25 mm; 1 ft = 30 cm; 1 sq yd = 0.8 m²; 1 acre = 0.4 ha
Note :   1. Prepare a hand log for each contract
         2. Monitor Schedule of Value by Contract

Figure 13-2. Schedule of Values Analysis.

PAYMENT INVOICE SUMMARY

TO: _____   PROJECT:_____

FROM:_____

CONTRACT FOR: _____ DATE:_____

1. Original Contract Sum $_____
2. Total Change Orders $_____
3. Total Contract Sum to Date $_____
4. Total Completed $_____
5. 10% Retainage of Total Completed $_____

6. Total Earned Less Retainage $_____
7. Less Previous Payments $_____

8. Current Payment Due $_____

9. Balance to Finish, Plus Retainage $_____

Contractor: _____
By: _____
Date: _____

State of: County of:
Subscribed and sworn to before me this   Day of
Notary Public:
My Commission expires:_____

Received By: _____ Date: _____
Release of Lien Attached:_____

Figure 13-3. Payment Invoice Summary.

AFFIDAVIT AND RELEASE OF LIEN

Before me the undersigned authority personally appeared. Who after being by me first duly sworn, deposes and says that:

1) He is _____ of _____ doing business in the State of _____, hereinafter called Contractor.

2) Contractor has heretofore furnished or caused to be furnished labor, material and/or services for the construction of certain improvements on the following described real property at

DESCRIPTION	INVOICE #	DATE	AMOUNT

3) Affiant represents that all persons and firms who furnished material, labor and/or services incident to the above have been paid in full except the following: (If no exception, insert the word NONE)

NAME	ADDRESS	AMOUNT DUE

4) The undersigned affiant for and in consideration of payment to contractor in the above invoice amount and all other previous payments paid to contractor, does hereby, for and in behalf of the contractor, waive, release, remise and relinquish the contractor's right to claim, demand, or impose a lien or liens for work done or material and/or services furnished or any other class of lien whatsoever, on the above described real property.

5) The affiant herein does hereby represent that he has authority to execute this Release of Lien for and in behalf of the contractor.

6) The affiant herein makes this Affidavit and Release of Lien for the express purpose of inducing _____, a Delawnre Corporation, to make payment and disbursement to the contractor in the amount stated above.

7) This Affidavit and Release of Lien is made by affiant with full knowledge of the applicable laws of the State of _____. In addition to such rights as may be afforded to under said applicable laws, affiant, individually and as authorized agent of contractor, expressly agrees to indemnify and save _____ harmless from any and all actual costs and expenses, including reasonable attorney's fees, arising out of claims by laborers, subcontractors or materialmen who might claim that they have not been paid for services or material furnished by or through the contractor on the above-described property.

8) The consideration for this Affidavit and Release of Lien is payment of the above-referenced invoice and is expressly conditioned on receipt of such payment.

SWORN to and subscribed before me
this day of

NOTARY PUBLIC   AFFIANT
My commission expires:

Figure 13-4. Affidavit and Release of Lien.

INITIATOR CHANGE ORDER REQUEST

Project Title_____

Project No._____ Contract No._____ Contract Date _____

Contractor _____   ☐ Owner

Proposed By:_____ Date _____   ☐ Engineer

Submitted By:_____ Date _____   ☐ Construction

Actual job conditions in area of proposed change:
_____
_____

Change order justification:
_____
_____
_____

Contractor authorized to proceed with this change ☐ YES ☐ NO on _____(Date)

Other contracts involved are as follows (List by Contract No.):_____Is Dwg Req?☐NO ☐YES_____
                                                                                    (SHEET NO.)

Description of Work to be Performed:

Figure 13-5. Initiator Change Order Request.

CHANGE ORDER CONTRACT

FORMING PART OF CONTRACT #_____   DATE:_____

EFFECTIVE DATE:_____   SUBCONTRACT #:_____

CONTRACTOR: XYZ_____   ADDENDUM #: _____

SUB-CONTRACTOR: _____   SUB-CONT PHONE:_____

VENDOR # _____   INDIVIDUAL CONTACT:_____

FOR WORK AT: _____

CATEGORY OF WORK:

1. DESCRIPTION AND SCOPE OF WORK:

2. SPECIFICATIONS
   All work shall be performed in accordance with the following specifications documents:
   A. XYZ General Conditions   Date:
   B. Municipal Utility Authority Specifications
   C. State DOT Standard Specifications for road and bridge construction

3. COMPENSATION

SUB-CONTRACTOR: CONTRACTOR: XYZ CORP
BY:_____   BY:_____
TITLE:_____   TITLE:_____
DATE:_____   DATE:_____
                                REVIEWED BY:_____
                                        DATE:_____
                                PREPARED BY:_____
                                        DATE:_____

Figure 13-6. Change Order Contract.

**LAND DEVELOPMENT
DAILY SURVEY REPORT**

CONSTRUCTION STAKING:

LOCATION:_____

      *CIRCLE ONE: Sewer Water Drainage Roadway Curbing Other*_____

HOURS CREW ON-SITE FROM _____ TO _____

                              TOTAL HOURS _____

STATION _____ TO _____

MONUMENTS: AMT. COMPLETE _____

LOCATION _____

      CIRCLE ONE: Sewer Water Drainage Roadway Curbing Misc. _____

HOURS CREW ON SITE FROM _____ TO _____

                              TOTAL HOURS _____

OTHER:

LOCATION: _____

REASON: _____

HOURS CREW ON SITE FROM _____ TO _____

                              TOTAL HOURS _____

Figure 14-1. Land Development Daily Survey Report.

LAND DEVELOPMENT DAILY CONSTRUCTION REPORT

PROJECT _____ DATE _____

COMMUNITY_____ DAY: S M T W TH F S

CONTRACTOR _____ WEATHER: CLEAR

                                                           OVERCAST   RAIN

COMPANY REP: _____ TEMP 0-32 32-50 50-70

                                                                  70-85   85+

AVERAGE FIELD FORCE / EQUIPMENT IN USE OF IDLED

QUANTITIES

LOCATION SEWER	MFG/GLASS	PIPE SIZE	AMT. PLACED	LATERALS LOT BLOCK	MANHOLE #	MISC

LOCATION DRAINAGE	TYPE	PIPE SIZE	AMT PLACED	INLET #	MANHOLE #	MISC

LOCATION WATER	PIPE SIZE	AMT PLACED	LATERALS LOT BLOCK	VALVES/TEES/PLUGS	FIRE HYDRANT

SUMMARY OF CONSTRUCTION ACTIVITIES

FIELD PROBLEMS (WHICH COULD RESULT IN DELAY OF CLAIM)

FOLLOW UP INSPECTIONS OF PREVIOUSLY REPORTED DEFICIENCIES

Figure 14-2. Land Development Daily Construction Report.

INSPECTOR'S WEEKLY REPORT

COMPLETED BY:_____

PROJECT:_____ DATE_____

CONTRACTOR:_____

SUBCONTRACTOR: _____

PROGRESS STATUS:

COMPLETE % _____   CONTRACTOR COMPLETE % _____
INCOMPLETE _____ INCOMPLETE _____

MATERIALS SUPPLIED THIS WEEK _____

PREVIOUSLY SUPPLIED:_____

TOTAL SUPPLIED TO DATE: _____

REMARKS:_____
_____
_____
_____
_____
_____
_____
_____
_____
_____
_____

Figure 14-3. Inspector's Weekly Report.

LAND DEVELOPMENT
ROADWAY CONSTRUCTION REPORT

PROJECT_____ DATE_____

COMMUNITY_____ DAY: S M T W TH F S

CONTRACTOR_____ WEATHER: CLEAR   RAIN
                                                            OVERCAST

CO. REP: _____ TEMP: 0-32   32-50   50-70
                                                           78-85   85+

STREET NAME _____ STATION _____ TO _____

	DEPTH CHECK	WIDTH CHECK	CBR	DENSITY
SUB-GRADE: (CIRCLE ONE) STABILIZED COMPACTED				
SUB-BASE: (CIRCLE ONE) ROAD GRAVEL QP S/C OTHER				
BASE: STABILIZED BASE - TYPE _____				
ASPHALT: FABC TYPE _____				

STREET _____ STATION _____ TO _____

SUB-GRADE: (CIRCLE ONE) STABILIZED COMPACTED				
SUB-BASE: (CIRCLE ONE) ROAD GRAVEL QP S/C OTHER				
BASE: STABILIZED BASE - TYPE _____				
ASPHALT: FABC TYPE _____				

MISCELLANEOUS

LOCATION:_____

PSI: _____ SLUMP:_____

TAKEN #: _____ BATCH #: _____

(CIRCLE ONE:)   Curb   Inlet   Flume   Other:_____

Figure 14-4. Land Development Roadway Construction Report.

Index